If I Could Tell You One Thing

*A collection of advice and pedagogical
insights from mathematics teachers*

Edited by Ed Southall

THE MATHEMATICAL ASSOCIATION

If I Could Tell You One Thing

This book is dedicated to everyone who has contributed their time and work towards providing the excellent resources offered by The Mathematical Association, with particular thanks to the authors involved in writing this book, and to Chris Pritchard for his guidance and advice throughout.

CONTENTS

1   *Introduction*

Ed Southall

The Mathematical Association has been supporting teachers of mathematics for 150 years. It's a remarkable milestone and just one of many reasons I am proud to be a member. It felt appropriate to mark this occasion in a way that would hopefully exemplify this purpose and pay tribute to the decades of guidance, advice and insights offered into the effective teaching of mathematics. As such, I am very pleased to present *If I could tell you one thing* – a collection of advice and pedagogical insights from mathematics teachers with a wide range of experiences and expertise.

What I love most about each chapter is the unmistakable joy of teaching maths that each author demonstrates through their words, their actions, and the expert knowledge they have built and fostered over the years. We all have so much to learn from each other in teaching and the opportunities to do so are often difficult to find or easy to miss. Teaching is hard and the journey towards mastering the art is long and never truly ends – we can only hope to continue to improve, learn from mistakes, fine tune our methods and learn from those who have taken similar journeys before us. Still, children possess wonderfully complicated, unique, and often unpredictable minds – so it's no surprise that in one moment we can feel as though we have finally found a perfect way to teach, to explain, to model, to assess, only to find that it doesn't work with the next class or the same class in the following lesson.

Therein lies both the frustrating difficulty of teaching and the wonderful intellectual pursuit of continuous self-improvement. I have taught on teacher training programmes for several years and have often struggled with the balance of teaching 'what you need to know' and 'what you need to know *now*'. There is so much to take in and so much nuance to consider when fine tuning your teaching practice, and whilst everything is important, I'm never quite sure of how much to expose trainees to in their first foray into the world of mathematics pedagogy. At the very least, my hope is that upon qualifying, teachers appreciate just how much there is to learn, and that a "training year" is just the beginning. Subject knowledge for example, is a continuous journey that never really ends.

For my first few years of teaching, I paid little attention to it beyond making sure I knew enough to get the answers and show others how to do the same. I felt at the time that my objective was simply to pass on the ability to tackle an exam paper, and in my naivety, I believed that the best way to do that was to memorise countless methods by any means possible – mostly rhymes and mnemonics. In all honesty I don't think I could have taught in any other way at that point. I was simply following the cycle – it's how I had been taught, and I hadn't been shown, or indeed seen, any other way of teaching maths.

It was only when I engaged with the wider maths community that I began to see so many things differently. I learned so much as soon as I decided I wanted to listen.

Experienced educators like Don Steward and Colin Foster gave me insights into the scientific precision of good task design and thought-provoking modelling of concepts, which in turn took me in several directions to gain deeper subject knowledge. My focus in teaching shifted to prioritise sense-making over answer-calculation, finding that the former shepherds the latter. From there I began to obsess over the etymology of the words of mathematics as I began to really see new connections – and, in turn, the importance of the precision of language in mathematics. This never-ending road of knowledge is indeed addictive. Learning theories, motivation strategies, visual represent-ations, textbook design – there is simply no end to our personal development and so many strands of teaching to explore. It can feel overwhelming but, put simply, I am content that I will always know more tomorrow than I do today.

I have been immersed in mathematics education for many years and written several books on the subject, yet I'm acutely aware I am far from what I would consider 'expert'. As the saying goes, the more you know, the more you realise you don't know. I hope the writings in this book give you inspiration, help you pursue new ideas, challenge your thinking, embolden your love of maths and maths teaching, or simply make you smile. I hope more than anything that this book inspires you to connect with others and share your own experiences, challenges, and success stories of teaching mathematics. We want to hear your voices too.

2   *Checking for Understanding*

Colin Foster

> In this chapter, I argue that 'checking for understanding' is impossible; all we can ever do is check for *mis*understandings. By using examples relating to Pythagoras' Theorem, I argue that *correct* answers are open to many interpretations, but *incorrect* answers (so long as the questions are well designed) can give really precise, valuable information about students' *mis*understandings. We can never conclude that a student has perfect understanding of something, but we can devise ever-trickier tasks that will find the weaknesses in their understanding, and, once we have found them, that's when the learning can begin.

Checking for understanding is impossible; all we can ever do is check for *mis*understandings. What do I mean by this?

Suppose we are interested in students' understandings of something like Pythagoras' Theorem. We could ask them to find the length of the missing side in Figure 1 [Note 1].

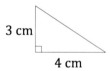

Figure 1: A 3-4-what triangle

Suppose they get this right, and say 5 cm. What does this tell us? I think it tells us very little. Maybe they know "a 3-4-5 triangle" as a thing, and so are just recalling this as a fact. Or maybe they are just mindlessly continuing the pattern 3, 4, ... and saying 5. Or maybe it was a lucky guess. Were they even attending to the fact that this is a *right-angled* triangle or that Pythagoras' Theorem was relevant? Have they even heard of Pythagoras' Theorem? Even if you ask the student to show their working or explain their answer (and even if they do so!), how do you know that they are not merely reproducing something that they have remembered, with little understanding involved. Getting a question right often tells us very little about a student's understanding. Getting a question *wrong*, on the other hand, can be much more informative about *mis*understandings, and I think this is what is really useful educationally.

Suppose that the student gets that question right. We could go on to ask them to find the missing length in Figure 2.

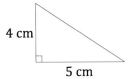

Figure 2: A 4-5-what triangle

If they answered "6 cm", that would give us a pretty clear idea that their misunderstanding was to do with simplistic pattern-following, based on the 3-4-5 from Figure 1. On the other hand, if they answered correctly, by calculating $\sqrt{4^2 + 5^2} = \sqrt{41}$ cm, I think this wouldn't tell us very much about their understanding of Pythagoras' Theorem. We can't tell from this answer how formulaic their knowledge might be, or how inert or inflexible it could prove itself under different circumstances. We don't learn much about their understanding until they get something *wrong*.

Let's suppose we go on to ask the student to find the missing length in something like Figure 3, where the required side is a leg, rather than the hypotenuse. If they calculated $\sqrt{5^2 + 6^2} = \sqrt{61}$ cm, then we could see exactly what was going wrong, as they would be failing to distinguish Figure 3 that they were given from Figure 4 that they weren't.

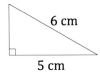

Figure 3: A 5-6-what triangle

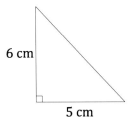

Figure 4: Another 5-6-what triangle

Alternatively, we might ask them whether they can find the missing length in something like Figure 5.

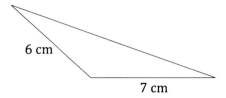

Figure 5: A 6-7-what triangle

This time, there is no right angle, so all that can be said is that, from the triangle inequality, the length of the third side must be somewhere between 7 – 6 = 1 cm and 6 + 7 = 13 cm, and without more information it is not possible to calculate an exact length. But, if the student were instead to answer $\sqrt{6^2 + 7^2} = \sqrt{85}$ cm, then we would learn something useful about the student: that they were not attending to the presence or absence of right angles in the triangles or to the uniqueness of the specified triangle [Note 2].

There is no limit to this ongoing task of posing increasingly demanding questions, stress-testing students' understanding until we find the cracks where it fails. If they get a task right, we resist jumping to conclusions about their understanding, and instead we pose something more challenging; if they get it wrong, we get valuable information that we can use to help them learn something.

Here are some tasks that, in different ways, surface different aspects of Pythagoras' Theorem, in some cases concealed within increasingly elaborate disguises:

1. Find the distance between (2, 10) and (5, 14).
2. Find the distance between (2, 10, 5) and (4, 13, 11).
3. Draw a line segment from (2, 10) to (5, 14).
   Add three more line segments to make a square.
   Find the area of the square.
4. The diagram in Figure 6 shows two concentric circles and a line segment of length 3 which is a tangent to the smaller circle.
   Find the area of the shaded annulus.

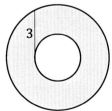

Figure 6: Two concentric circles

5. A ladder of length 13 feet is standing upright against a wall.
    If the top end of the ladder slides down the wall 1 foot, how far
    out from the wall will the bottom end move?
6. A cable 1 km long is lying flat along the ground, with its ends
    fixed.
    If its length is increased by 1 m, but the ends are still fixed 1 km
    apart, how high up can the midpoint of the cable be raised before
    the cable becomes taut?
7. I am standing in a rectangular hall, and my distances from three
    of the corners are 6 m, 9 m and 10 m.
    How far am I from the fourth corner? [Note 3]
8. What is the shortest distance from one corner of a 3 × 5 × 6
    cuboid to the opposite corner, *travelling only along the surface of
    the cuboid?* (See Foster, 2019)

Successfully answering any or all of these questions does not, I think, in
any sense 'prove' understanding of Pythagoras' Theorem. I think we
should never conclude that a student 'understands', because there is
always another question that might be asked, some change that might be
made that *would* trip them up. You never get to the point where you are
justified in placing a tick in a spreadsheet against "Understands
Pythagoras' Theorem". No one ever has total understanding of anything
in every conceivable situation. But this is OK. What matters in
educational terms is that *failure* with any of these questions *does* reveal
students' limitations, and provides opportunities to deepen the
understanding that exists.

The idea that a student getting a question correct may mean very little,
whereas wrong answers can be highly informative, is for me reminiscent
of Karl Popper's philosophy of *falsificationism* (see Dienes, 2008, for a
nice summary). You are constantly trying to falsify your belief that the
student understands something by throwing increasingly tricky
questions at them. If the question succeeds in tripping them up, you have
succeeded in discovering a weakness in their understanding. We all have
weak spots in our understanding, and all it takes is a well-designed
question to surface those weaknesses and make them visible – so that
we can do something about them. If the question fails to trip up the
student, you don't conclude that the student 'has understanding'; you
throw them a trickier question. When a student gets something right, we
are of course pleased, but we don't draw sweeping conclusions from it;
when they are wrong, provided the question was well designed, we have
positive evidence of a difficulty that we can then address. This means
that the job of learning is never finished; there is always another
question to be posed. But, viewed this way, testing is not the enemy of

learning. Constantly testing students by offering them challenging questions and tasks is precisely how we uncover difficulties that we can then subsequently address.

It may seem unkind to try to trip up your students, but actually it isn't. An analogy I sometimes use relates to an occasion when I was fitting shelves to the wall in my study. I carefully screwed up the brackets, and then, before loading the shelves with all my books, I pulled as hard as I could on the brackets to see if I could pull them down. I had just put the brackets up, so, in a sense, of course I didn't want them to come down. But I tried *really hard* to pull them down. If they were going to come down, I would rather that they did so now than after I had carefully arranged all my books on them! So, I was not pulling just a little bit, so as to be gentle with my precious handiwork: I was pulling as hard as I could. For me, this speaks to the idea that robust testing is the kindest thing to do. Failing to test those brackets at that point is setting up the shelves for far more disastrous failure later. Likewise, failing to test students properly when we teach them something is not being kind; it is almost guaranteeing that later on (whether this is when they are at home, trying to do their homework unaided, or in a high-stakes examination situation) they are going to come unstuck – and there will be no one there to help them then. Far better to come unstuck in the safety of the classroom, where difficulties can be addressed in a supportive environment. So, we don't give students easy challenges that we are confident they will succeed on; we test hard to find the weaknesses, so that we can help them.

In his closing address at the 1997 Association of Teachers of Mathematics Conference, Phil Boorman (1997, p. 40) talked about reconceiving his role as a teacher away from making things easy: "My job was to find a suitable field for [the students] to explore and to sit up on the hillside above and roll down rocks for the kids to jump or climb or scramble over." Rather than smoothing the path in front of them (Wigley, 1992), the teacher's job is to make life *difficult* for the students, throwing them challenges that are well-judged and will test and hone their skills. It is a battle between student and question. When the student wins over the question, that can be motivating for them, and of course we want to celebrate that, but when the question wins over the student, that is when the learning opportunities materialise.

Of course, this doesn't apply to high-stakes examinations. In those situations, we obviously hope that students will get the questions right, but a high-stakes examination is not a learning situation. In a learning situation, we shouldn't be asking a question or posing a task hoping, wishing and praying that they'll get it right, hinting towards the right answer with little verbal and non-verbal nudges. A right answer tells us very little – maybe just that our question was too easy? Right answers are great mathematically – I disagree with telling students that getting the right answer doesn't matter – but *wrong* answers are the useful ones pedagogically. If the teacher sees wrong answers as annoying but inevitable interruptions to the flow of the lesson, that use up precious classroom time, their priority will be to try to minimise the disturbance and avoid the lesson being derailed, so they can get back on track as quickly as possible. But, if we see our questions as deliberately seeking to catch the students – yes, 'trick questions', even – then we will be delighted when one of these questions succeeds, and our conjecture that students might struggle with it is borne out.

Diagnosing a disease is a positive thing when a treatment is available, and should not be something to fear. If you wish to learn, then you want to have your difficulties exposed, so you can enjoy thinking about them and become more competent – this is the culture we need to cultivate: *"Getting something wrong is great – it means you're about to learn something!"* I have heard teachers being given the advice to "Try not to show your disappointment when a student gets something wrong". Even better than this, I would say, *"Don't actually be disappointed!"*

Notes

1. The figures in this article are deliberately not drawn to scale.
2. Of course, although the figures are not drawn to scale, the student might interpret Figure 5 as clearly indicating an obtuse-angled triangle, and therefore might conclude that the missing side must be *greater than $\sqrt{6^2 + 7^2} = \sqrt{85}$* cm.
3. See Foster (2003) for solutions to Questions 5-7.

Acknowledgement

Parts of this chapter are based on a plenary I gave at the Mathematical Association Annual Conference in April 2021.

References

Boorman, P. (1997). 'Believing is seeing', *Mathematics Teaching*, 160, 38-43.
Dienes, Z. (2008). *Understanding psychology as a science: An introduction to scientific and statistical inference*. Palgrave Macmillan.

Foster, C. (2003). *Instant Maths Ideas for Key Stage 3 Teachers: Shape and space*. Cheltenham: Nelson Thornes.
www.foster77.co.uk/instantmathsideas.htm
www.foster77.co.uk/2.07%20Pythagoras'%20Theorem.pdf
Foster, C. (2019). Spider on a cuboid. *Teach Secondary*, *8*(6), 116–117.
www.foster77.co.uk/Foster,%20Teach%20Secondary,%20Spider %20on%20a%20cuboid.pdf
Wigley, A. (1992). 'Models for teaching mathematics', *Mathematics Teaching*, 141, 4-7.

3   *Times Tables*

Daniel Griller

Times tables? But we know all about this. We did them in primary school!

Probably not like this. But let's begin with a warm-up.

1. Calculate $1 + 2 + 3 + \cdots + 1000$.

Easy.

Okay. How about this?

2. Let n be a positive integer. Find a simple closed-form expression for $1 + 2 + 3 + \cdots + n$.

Done. It's the same as the first one!

Not quite. The first can be solved with brute force, given enough time. The second needs something cleverer. Anyway, let's kick things up a notch.

3. What is the sum of the positive multiples of 7 less than 1000?

Still pretty easy. Do you have anything more difficult?

In good time. How about this?

4. Which is greater: the sum of the positive multiples of 4 less than 1,000,000, or the sum of the positive multiples of 8 less than 1,000,000?

That was easier than the last one! Big numbers don't make it more difficult.

If you say so. I'm not sure everyone would agree. Next question:

5. Which is greater: the sum of the positive even numbers less than 1,000,000, or the sum of the positive multiples of 3 less than 1,000,000?

Now we're getting somewhere! I had to do some thinking. Good question!

I'm glad you approve! What about this?

6. Let A_n be the sum of the positive multiples of 999 less than or equal to n, and let B_n be the sum of the positive multiples of 1000 less than or equal to n. What is the greatest value of n for which $A_n < B_n$?

What?!

What? You said you wanted something more difficult!

*Yeah, but this is ridiculous! How are we supposed to solve **that**?*

You tell me – that's part of the puzzle.

Fine. This could take a while…

Solutions

1. If we pair up the first and last terms, the second and penultimate terms, and so on, we have

$$1 + 2 + 3 + \cdots + 1000$$
$$= (1 + 1000) + (2 + 999) + (3 + 998) + \cdots + (500 + 501)$$
$$= 1001 \times 500$$
$$= \mathbf{500500}.$$

2. If n is even, we can use a similar idea to the previous problem:
$$1 + 2 + 3 + \cdots + n$$
$$= (1 + n) + (2 + (n - 1)) + (3 + (n - 2)) + \cdots$$
$$+ \left(\frac{n}{2} + \left(\frac{n}{2} + 1 \right) \right)$$
$$= (n + 1) \times \frac{n}{2}$$
$$= \frac{n(n + 1)}{2}.$$

If n is odd, the argument is almost identical:
$$1 + 2 + 3 + \cdots + n$$
$$= (1 + n) + \left(2 + (n - 1) \right) + \left(3 + (n - 2) \right) + \cdots$$
$$+ \left(\frac{n - 1}{2} + \frac{n + 3}{2} \right) + \frac{n + 1}{2}$$
$$= (n + 1) \times \frac{n - 1}{2} + \frac{n + 1}{2}$$
$$= \frac{n + 1}{2} (n - 1 + 1)$$

$$= \frac{n(n+1)}{2}.$$

Therefore, $1 + 2 + 3 + \cdots + n = \dfrac{\boldsymbol{n(n+1)}}{\boldsymbol{2}}.$

3. We have $1000 \div 7 = 142$, remainder 6.
Using the previous result, we have

$$7 \times 1 + 7 \times 2 + 7 \times 3 + \cdots + 7 \times 142$$
$$= 7(1 + 2 + 3 + \cdots + 142)$$
$$= \frac{7(142)(143)}{2}$$
$$= \boldsymbol{71071}.$$

4. We need not calculate each sum. Every multiple of 8 is also a multiple of 4, but there are lots of multiples of 4 that are not multiples of 8, such as 4, 12 and 20.

So the first sum contains every term in the second sum, and several more positive terms besides. Hence the **multiples of 4** have the greater sum.

5. Consider blocks of consecutive integers of the form
$$6n + 1, 6n + 2, 6n + 3, \dots, 6n + 6.$$

The sum of the even numbers in this block is
$$(6n + 2) + (6n + 4) + (6n + 6) = 18n + 12.$$

The sum of the multiples of 3 in this block is
$$(6n + 3) + (6n + 6) = 12n + 9.$$

Now split the numbers from 1 to 999,996 into blocks of this form:

$$(1,2,3,4,5,6), (7,8,9,10,11,12), (13,14,15,16,17,18),$$
$$\dots (999991,999992,999993,999994,999995,999996).$$

The first block corresponds to $n = 0$, the second block to $n = 1$, and so on.

It is clear that for $n \geq 0$, we have $18n + 12 > 12n + 9$. So in each block, the sum of the even numbers is greater than the sum of the multiples of 3. It follows that, between 1 and 999996, the sum of the even numbers vastly exceeds the sum of the multiples of 3.

Finally, the sum of the even numbers between 999997 and 999999 inclusive is 999998, and the sum of the multiples of 3 between 999997 and 999999 is 999999. The difference between these sums is 1, and will hardly make a dent in the huge debt the multiples of 3 have already accrued up to this point.

Hence the **even numbers** less than 1,000,000 have the greater sum.

6. Suppose $A_n < B_n$. Then the inequality still holds if we replace n with the greatest multiple of 1000 less than or equal to n, say $1000b$:

$$A_{1000b} < B_{1000b}.$$

Now let $999a$ be the largest multiple of 999 less than or equal to $1000b$. Then $999a \leq 1000b$ but $999(a + 1) > 1000b$.

Since a is the number of multiples of 999 up to and including $1000b$, and b is the number of multiples of 1000 up to and including $1000b$, and $999 < 1000$, it is certainly the case that $a \geq b$. (This just says that there are at least as many multiples of 999 up to some point as there are multiples of 1000.)

But can a be greater than b?

Suppose $a \geq b + 1$. From above, we have $999(a + 1) > 1000b$. All quantities on both sides of these inequalities are positive, so we can multiply the inequalities:

$$999a(a + 1) > 1000b(b + 1).$$

The expressions appearing here look similar to earlier work. Halving both sides yields

$$999 \times \frac{a(a + 1)}{2} > 1000 \times \frac{b(b + 1)}{2}.$$

This can be reinterpreted:

$$999(1 + 2 + 3 + \cdots + a) > 1000(1 + 2 + 3 + \cdots + b)$$

$$A_{999a} > B_{1000b}.$$

Now we have a problem. $999a$ was chosen to be the largest multiple of 999 less than or equal to $1000b$; there are no multiples of 999 between $999a$ and $1000b$.

So $A_{999a} = A_{1000b}$ and hence $A_{1000b} > B_{1000b}$.

This contradicts an inequality at the start of this argument.
So in fact we have that $a = b$.
This says something quite strong – if the sum of the multiples of 999 up to some point is less than the sum of the multiples of 1000 up to the same point, then there are the same number of multiples of each. Eventually the number of multiples of 999 will be beyond the reach of the number of multiples of 1000; so the question is well-posed, and a greatest possible value of n does indeed exist.

To finish off the job, we will again use that $999(a + 1) > 1000b$.
Since $a = b$, we have

$$999(b + 1) > 1000b$$
$$999b + 999 > 1000b$$
$$b < 999.$$

So $a = b \leq 998$.

Maximising b will yield the maximum value of n (the more multiples of 1000 there are, the further we have to look through the number line).

Does $a = b = 998$ lead anywhere useful?
Some useful calculations:

$$999^2 = 998001,$$
$$998 \times 1000 = 998000 = 999^2 - 1.$$

So there are 998 multiples of 999 less than or equal to 998000, and also 998 multiples of 1000 less than or equal to 998000. But the moment we look beyond this, at 998001, we hit 999 multiples of 999, so that $a = 999$, which is too big.

Thus the greatest possible value of n is **998000**.

4   *Lessons from a Million Subscribers*

Eddie Woo

The most effective teachers are often the most persistent learners. This has been one of my core convictions since beginning my journey as an educator, and I particularly like the way that New Jersey librarian John Cotton Dana put it. When asked to supply a quote suitable for inscription on a new building at Newark State College, he wrote the powerful words: "Who dares to teach must never cease to learn."

I especially love learning things from my students. Since my first year of teaching, I've made a point to ensure that everyone in my classes knows that I am the lead learner in the classroom – not some infallible fount of knowledge, but someone always humble enough to discover new things, even from those people I'm responsible to teach. And I'm seldom disappointed: I can't think of a single group of students I've ever taught where I didn't learn something new because of them. It might be a new way to solve an old problem, like when one of my students looked at a geometry problem designed to strengthen algebraic reasoning and literally took it apart with a pair of scissors that rendered the problem delightfully straightforward with no algebra necessary. It might be a helpful metaphor for explaining a curly concept, like when an old student of mine explained subtraction of negative numbers by appealing to scenes in the animated film *Up* where the main characters add balloons (positive numbers) to make their house rise, but also achieve the same effect by subtracting furniture (negative numbers) which were weighing the house down.

Sometimes, the things that I learn from my students are not so direct. It is less a matter of them explicitly telling me something I didn't know, and more a matter of me discovering something through them by accident. I vividly remember one of these moments happening in my very first year of teaching, when I planned a lesson on how to differentiate functions from first principles. Walking into that classroom, I distinctly remember feeling a confidence so deep that it was matched only by how much of a train wreck the lesson became. I had originally thought: "How hard could this be? I understand the idea myself, so I'll just show them how I do it and then they'll understand it too." But the confused looks of my students at the end of my explanation taught me that I'd not only missed the mark on this lesson – they taught me that I needed to reconfigure my entire approach to helping students develop understanding of a new concept.

For the last few years, I've had the privilege of a very large set of students to learn from. That's because I once taught a student who was diagnosed with cancer and was unable to attend school, so to help him continue learning I began to film my regular classroom lessons and publish them on YouTube. I never expected anyone beyond that one student to watch, which accounts for why the production values in my early videos are so horrendously low. However, fast forward to now and (shockingly) over a million people from all around the world have clicked the little red button that says "subscribe". By voting with their views and likes, they've taught me some interesting and slightly surprising things – so here, I present to you three brief lessons I've learned from the people I get to teach through the wonder of the internet, through the lens of some of my most popular videos.

1. Cultivate the desire for why, then feed it

One of the most powerful aspects of learning mathematics is that, in large part, we can always point to a reason for the ideas and concepts that we are learning. But this isn't always our students' experience. In fact, repeatedly people watch my videos because their journey of learning mathematics has often felt like they were taught to accept things without knowing why. On my video *Dividing by zero?* (5.6 million views), users commented:

> *Meanwhile, other people ask why all numbers can't be divided by zero, and their teachers say "because you shouldn't!"*

> *Damn this guy really just destroyed a math question I've had all these years ... without using limits or graphs explanation till the very end. My teacher be like: just look at the graph.*

> *Literally, we were just taught it's undefined, never taught why.*

There are practical reasons we often do this as teachers – if we stopped for every single curious question in a classroom environment, we'd probably not get very far on any given day! But if accepting concepts without reasoning becomes a characteristic feature of our lessons, then that is a betrayal of mathematical thinking and an indictment on our pedagogical priorities.

A particularly common place that this happens is when we teach our students about formulas. Formulas are dangerous for the same reason that they are powerful: they can often be used without the user knowing why they work or where they came from! And this is a state of play that is clear from some of the people who commented on my video, *Visual Proof of Pythagoras' Theorem* (2.5 million views):

> *This is the only teacher I've seen who actually explains what the theorems mean rather than making the students just memorise the formula with no understanding of what they're actually memorising.*

> *67 years old and finally understand what my math teacher was trying to tell me about Pythagoras. Where was this guy 53 years ago!*

> *Damn I really wish I was in his class. At least this way, I actually do understand why these theorems exist and not just knowing because it's a formula, but because there's an actual reason for it.*

In this lesson, I was not doing anything extraordinary. I was simply using coloured cardboard to help me re-enact one of the classic dissection proofs for Pythagoras' Theorem. However, the hundreds of people who wrote comments just like the ones above are obviously evidence of how many people around the world have learned this beautiful result without ever realising that it is even more wonderful when you see not just that it is true, but why it is true.

2. Find the story, then tell it as it deserves

Though I enrolled in a degree that put me on the path to becoming a mathematics teacher from my first day in university, mathematics was not always a subject that I loved. In my senior years of high school, my studies were far more focused on the humanities: English, history and drama. In my early days teaching maths, I thought that my love for narrative structure and the power of a good story would have to take a back seat as I focused on numbers and patterns. I couldn't have been more wrong, and it's with delight that I've discovered that mathematics is often best learned when we can find a compelling story to illustrate the concept that we are seeking to explain.

This was certainly the case when I was teaching a unit on statistics, which included explicit reference to the various kinds of bias that can enter a data set before any kind of analysis or evaluation can take place. In my video on *Survivorship Bias* (2.8 million views), viewers wrote:

This has to be fake, I've never seen a classroom this engaged.

This man's really tricked me into being in class on my free time.

I enjoyed his presentation performance. Theatrical, almost. Odd realizing my early childhood teachers were giving amazing body language performance and presentations that were as meaningful and learnful as possible to young learners.

The focus of this portion of the lesson was on the classic story of Abraham Wald, the statistician who led the analysis of US Army data on where planes were receiving damage and where they ought to be armoured. The story of his insight, a delightful emblem of survivorship bias and its pervasive effect on the data we observe around us, is compelling and memorable. Stories that illustrate the surprising and counterintuitive power of mathematics are worth telling before, during and after moments where we focus on the formulas and equations.

3.   Anticipate the open door

In a hundred years, I would never have guessed the most popular video on my channel – and the margin of its popularity is wide. The most viewed lesson that I ever uploaded is called *Why is 0 factorial equal to 1?* It's been viewed over 11 million times, which boggles my mind considering it is just a snippet out of an otherwise very ordinary lesson. One commenter was just as surprised as I was:

I can't believe I'm watching this video for entertainment.

I'm sure that this video resonates with many partly because of the first idea I mentioned in this list, namely, that it explains a result that most have learned to accept as inscrutable. But the thing that I've learned from this video's popularity is quite different, and isn't visible just from watching the video itself. Part of what amazes me about this part of the lesson is that I wasn't planning to say any of it.

I had a lesson plan written in my teaching diary that day, and I'd gone through most of it successfully. But as we neared the end of the lesson, a student asked a question that wasn't in my "script". I might have dismissed the question to be addressed in a future lesson, but one of her peers expressed curiosity to know the answer. Then others chimed in and suddenly I realised that I had an opportunity on my hands. A door for learning was squeaking its way open and I was standing there with the choice of opening it or walking past it.

As evidenced by the existence of this video, I opened it wide and had a merry time. But I could not have done this unless I'd at least partly anticipated that this was a likely question and had my thoughts in order to explore it playfully with the class. As any jazz musician will tell you, great improvisation is not merely made up on the spot (even if it is to some measure); such creativity only sprouts in the soil that is carefully tilled by countless hours of deliberate thought and practice. Let's apply ourselves with the same diligence to be ready for that door when it opens.

5   *Introducing Trigonometry*

Martin Noon

During my twenty or so years of teaching maths, I've used lots of the cliché techniques for teaching trigonometry, from measuring triangles, using formula triangles, making up funny (and some rude) phrases for SOHCAHTOA. But I was never happy that when I then got on to teaching non-right-angled triangles at GCSE or solving trigonometric functions at A level, it felt like I was teaching distinct topics. It was annoying that their knowledge of trigonometry didn't seem to flow.

I trialled something with a middle set year 10 class that had never seen trigonometry before. I carefully planned a series of lessons to ensure we had covered similar triangles and spent some time thinking about scale factors and enlargements. We practised enlarging right-angled triangles with known sides, used Pythagoras' Theorem to find missing sides, combined the two topics and we were then ready for my new approach to trigonometry.

I had created a Trigonometry Calculator. Each pupil would get the first quadrant of the unit circle which I had managed to overlay with part of a protractor. They could use a ruler to go from the origin, through an angle of choice, to create a right-angled triangle and read off the scales to find the height and base.

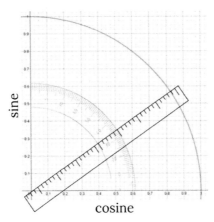

I had a PowerPoint to demonstrate to the class how to use it. The Trigonometry Calculator would always have a hypotenuse of length 1, therefore, if they read off the scale an estimate for the height and base of the triangle for the angle they needed, they could then apply the appropriate scale factor for an enlarged version. I didn't even talk about sine and cosine at first, we just talked about heights and bases and picked different angles to try.

For a class that were difficult to manage at times, they did great. We made it completely non-calculator to help them practise their decimal multiplication skills.

I then introduced the phrases sine and cosine and the funny Greek letter theta. We were able to generalise the enlargements, purposely tweaking the diagram to a different orientation.

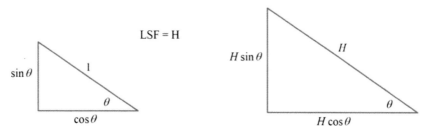

I had a worksheet for them to find estimates, and then use them to find missing sides of triangles.

<u>Estimating using the Trigonometry Calculator</u>

Section A - Estimate to 2 decimal places

1) sin 30
2) cos 30
3) sin 45
4) cos 45
5) sin 60
6) cos 60
7) sin 20
8) cos 70
9) sin 50
10) cos 63
11) sin 25
12) cos 75

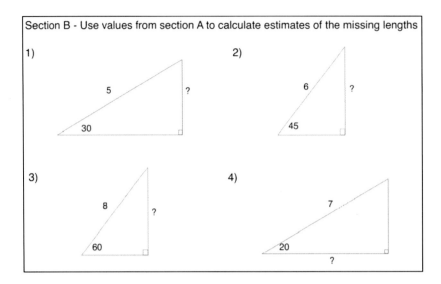

Section B - Use values from section A to calculate estimates of the missing lengths

1)

5   ?

30

2)

6   ?

45

3)

8   ?

60

4)

7

20

?

They were able to find missing legs, missing hypotenuses, we even went backwards, and estimated angles given the hypotenuse and a side.

We ventured on to the type where you would use tan, but just used Pythagoras to find the hypotenuse and then used our previous methods. After a couple of lessons using the trig calculator and the pupils noticing the buttons on their own calculator, I then showed them how to find more accurate values. They asked what "tan" was and I showed them how it would help them with the triangles involving just the opposite and adjacent.

The class had a much better grounding of the topic than I expected after this. They were not reliant on remembering SOHCAHTOA. They didn't feel the need to use the formula triangles. I was happy, they were happy.

This experiment got me thinking. Why not go a step further? Why not introduce the unit circle earlier? It would lead into plotting the graphs nicely and it would introduce the concept of applying trigonometric functions to obtuse and reflex angles. So since then, I have made a point of introducing trigonometry to a class with the unit circle. There are countless *GeoGebra* applets available showing the right-angled triangles formed from different angles or it's fairly straightforward to do the same thing on *Desmos*.

I will still use my trig calculator briefly and get a class to estimate and then check values with their calculator.

I will show how the tangent can be found by an enlargement of scale factor $\frac{1}{\cos\theta}$, which can then be used to discuss the meaning of the word tangent. This can open up discussions about secant, cosecant, cotangents, depending on the group!

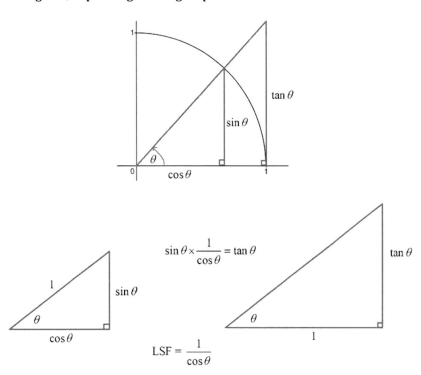

At school, I have used this introduction with year 9 and year 10, and have seen the effect it has when again teaching some of the same pupils at A level. Their understanding of trigonometry is stronger. They are able to find solutions to trigonometric functions quicker, and they can switch between using the unit circle or graphs to find solutions in the interval required much easier than a group having seen these links for the first time in year 12.

During lockdown in 2020 I used this approach with my own children. My daughter was in year eight at the time and had finished her remote maths work, my son was set to start secondary school in September. We did some trigonometry for fun. I showed them the unit circle. We estimated some values using my trig calculator, we found some missing sides using a scientific calculator. They did great and they found it fun.

It is clear to me that we could go into a lot more depth as to where the mathematics comes from at a much earlier age. We could be talking more about the history behind the concepts, and then spend more time using some of the amazing technology available to explore this mathematics much earlier on than we do currently.

While working in educational publishing, alongside teaching, I have been fortunate to help write mathematics teaching content for other countries. I have seen the differences between the notation used but more importantly the striving for a depth of mathematical understanding in their students. While attending UK mathematics teaching conferences, I have seen evidence that primary-aged children can tackle some very advanced mathematical concepts if the questions are framed correctly. These experiences have made me rethink my approach to many topics. Maybe I'll get them all perfect after another twenty years!

6   *Images for Teaching Statistics*

Tom Francome

The whole point of representing data using charts and diagrams is to make interpreting the information simpler. Images are powerful because they are often instant. Could we be making more use of images in the teaching of school statistics to understand the concepts behind various ideas on the curriculum? Here I offer some images for connecting ideas in school-level statistics.

It's quite common to think of representing data as involving images. We recognise that bar charts, box plots, and scatter plots can often be more intuitive for those interpreting data than tables of values, but how much attention do teachers' pay to images when teaching the concepts of statistics in schools? In simple cases such as the tally chart pupils can see clearly how the chart appears from the data. How might similar work be done to make other statistical representations transparent?

Averages

A classic context to think about averages in the classroom is working out the average height of the class. A possible approach is to place everyone in height order and cross off pupils from either end until you get to the middle. Many teachers use this 'crossing off' image for the median. Incidentally, when there are two items I find it helpful to think about what would be halfway between them. Yes, I know you can calculate the arithmetic mean but I've seen this taught as just another procedure to remember without developing an intuitive understanding that strengthens the concept of median as middle. It certainly hasn't been obvious to all the pupils I've worked with that when $n = 2$, the mean is equal to the median.

Mean

With the mean there are at least two images that need attention: firstly, the idea of collecting together and sharing out equally, and secondly, the idea of 'evening out'. The second image can be overlooked: in Western mathematics there can be a tendency to focus on representations closest to the procedure taught, for example, Ma (1999) found US teachers focused on representations of subtraction that aligned best with the algorithm they would teach whereas Chinese teachers used representations that helped develop the concept (Note 1). Ideally, we want to offer representations that support both procedures and concepts.

A favourite context for developing the concept of averages is sharing out juice. I got this idea from Don Steward, but you can find similar approaches in Japanese textbooks such as Tokyo Shoseki's Mathematics International series (Note 2). I have heard teachers call such things a 'pseudo-context' and question whether this is something that people do in 'real-life'. However, as is often the case, the context here makes the mathematics "realisable" (Geoff Wake, Note 3). The "realistic" in the Dutch 'Realistic Mathematics Education' is sometimes misconstrued as implying an everyday occurrence however "realisable" feels a much closer translation of the intended meaning in that learners can imagine the situation (Note 4). Even very young children have familiarity with sharing fairly, often before multiplication. Mathematics should make sense and, the context here can be used to make sense of what the problem *is*, and how the mathematics helps us solve it. It is worth thinking more generally about when a context might help make the mathematics more meaningful and avoid algorithms becoming a senseless procedure for some learners.

We might have a recipe that requires orange juice and want to know how much juice you get from a typical orange. If you haven't freshly squeezed your own juice you'll be disappointed to know you need more oranges than you might think, so you might want to know if each orange produced the same amount of juice, how many oranges you would need. The context focuses attention on the idea of average as a 'best estimate' or a 'representative value'. Suppose we squeeze a few oranges and get the following results: 55 ml, 80 ml, 60 ml, 75 ml, 60 ml, 90 ml. A visual representation like Figure 1 is helpful here.

We can see at a glance that there are a couple that are the same height and grouping them in height order as in Figure 2 makes this even more apparent, though the numbers are small here, so this most common value (60 ml) isn't *that* representative as half the oranges contain more juice than this. Having the juices in order allows us to play our median game from before where we try and work out the middle value, crossing off from either end. As we have an even number, the context of juice helps to make sense of the kind of 'evening out' that is required to find the 'middle' value between the 60 ml and 75 ml – 'we need to tip a bit of the 75 ml into the 60 ml to make them the same, how much?'

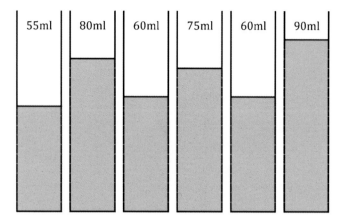

Figure 1: amounts of juice in six oranges

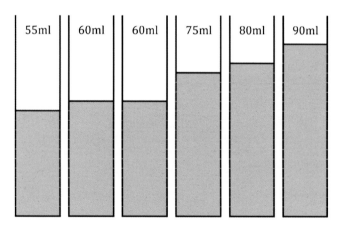

Figure 2: juice from six oranges in ascending order

Learners might think about how much should end up in each as the middle value between them, splitting the difference and adding from the taller to the smaller or collecting the juice into a larger jug and sharing it out equally. This approach using juice gives a nice way into thinking about evening out the amount of juice in the two middle cups, which can develop intuition of what the mean means. This can be extended to think about how the evening out might work for all six oranges as in Figure 3. Actual orange juice can be used, or it can be represented with counters or multilink cubes. Focusing on this allows students to make sense of why you might add up all the numbers and then share out equally.

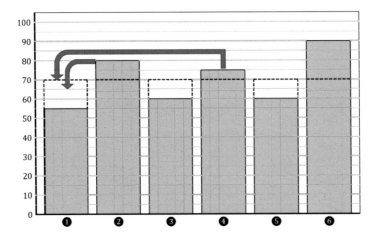

Figure 3: 'Evening out' the juice in six oranges, for example
by pouring 10ml from 2nd and 5ml from the 4th into the 1st

Whilst I think contexts *can* add meaning and aid understanding, one of
the ways mathematics gains its power is by abstracting away from the
context. Of course, I wouldn't be happy if pupils could only solve
problems about oranges and there is a lot of lovely mathematics that can
come from working on averages without contexts which still can focus
on meaning. For example, finding all the sets of five positive integers
where the mode is 3, the median is 3 and the mean is 4.

These kinds of task can be represented concretely with cubes or
pictorially with squares on paper (as in Figure 4) or with line lengths.
The mean can be visualised as evening out as before or as adding all the
parts together and dividing.

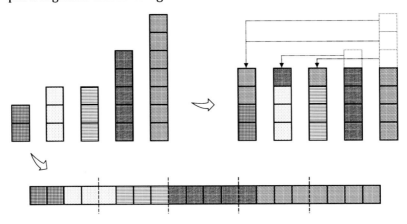

Figure 4: Finding the mean of 2, 3, 3, 5, 7
by 'evening out' and 'equal sharing'.

28

I find aligning the blocks (as in Figure 4) to be quite a powerful image. It can be related to the number line which is already a powerful didactical device that can be used in a variety of contexts to support and develop thinking, but it can also be used to illustrate the connections between other statistical representations such as pie charts and cumulative frequency diagrams and help learners make sense of what they're doing.

Frequency to cumulative frequency

An image I have found helpful for understanding cumulative frequency is to take the bars in a frequency diagram and raise each to where the previous ends. Obviously, describing this is less clear than an image like Figure 5. The cumulative frequency polygon comes from drawing the diagonals. For me, this helps make sense of how the data accumulates in a way that can be obscured by just following some rules to produce a table.

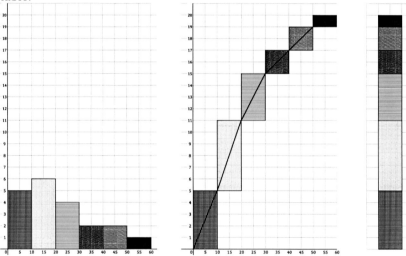

Figure 5: Connections between frequency diagram, cumulative frequency, and composite bar chart.

Combining images such as this into a composite bar chart also offers some insights as this can be used to show percentages or proportions. As with most representations of data they are especially useful when making comparisons: perhaps within the same chart or between two or more charts. Composite bar charts connect nicely to, and can help make sense of, what is happening in a pie chart. Many people love to hate pie charts, and some suggest they "should never be used" (Tufte, 1983, p.178; see Note 5 below)– circle segments are hard to visually compare, particularly if there are more than two, and often alternative charts can represent data more clearly. But whilst pie charts are on the curriculum and in the newspapers everyone needs to work with them and, if that is the case, then they ought to make sense. If the bars representing your data are drawn on paper then combined into a composite bar, then this can be cut out and 'wrapped around' into a circle and the edges joined up to form a pie chart. It is in an interesting (if challenging) task to try and recreate this by construction or with dynamic geometry but this is another area where I think concrete representations can be helpful.

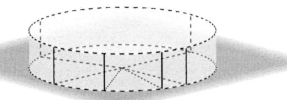

Figure 6: Pie chart created by 'wrapping around' a composite bar chart

If we revisit the counters or cubes used to play about with averages in Figure 4 we might imagine reorganising those to form an n-sided regular polygon as in Figure 7. We just need to find the centre and add some pie cuts and we now have a helpful mental model for how a pie chart works without having to focus initially on all of those calculation steps. This works even better if you arrange your circle over an empty protractor (Note 6). This kind of task can help to develop the conceptual understanding of the underlying mathematical structure of a pie chart. This can be further aided by using a realisable context and a purpose. Many mathematics teachers will be familiar with investigating Smarties and this might often mean: empty out a box, make a bar chart/pictogram and perhaps use the data to draw a pie chart (Note 7). However, you can also use the Smarties to create a physical model of the mathematical situation as in Figure 8.

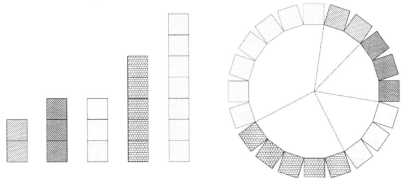

Figure 7: Rearranging discrete values into a pie chart

I've found that imagery like this and as described in the rest of this article can be a really powerful way to smooth the transition to more formal ideas. We use visual representations of data to help make sense of the data. We should think about how we can use visual imagery to help students make sense of the mathematics. We should also think hard about when contexts might help, and when they might hinder. Whatever you're teaching, it's worth thinking carefully about what images you offer.

Figure 8: contents of a packet of *Smarties* represented as a pie chart

Notes

(1) Ma, L. (1999). *Knowing and Teaching Elementary Mathematics: Teachers' Understanding of Fundamental Mathematics in China and the United States.* Lawrence Erlbaum Associates Mahwah, NJ.

(2) Fujii, T. & Iitaka, S. (2013). *Mathematics International Grade 5 (English Translation).* Tokyo, Japan: Tokyo Shoseki, pp.A84-A86., **www.globaledresources.com**

(3) Wake, G. (1994) 'Making sense of and with mathematics: the interface between academic mathematics and mathematics in practice', *Educational Studies in Mathematics*, 86(2), 271–290.

(4) Finding the length of a ladder leaned against a wall is another such context, helpful not because pupils regularly need to do this (in fact, you normally buy ladders based on their length) but rather because you can imagine the situation and the ladder forming a right-triangle with the wall and the floor.

(5) Tufte, E. R. (1983). *The Visual Display of Quantitative Information.* Cheshire, CT: Graphics Press.

(6) Francome, T. (2016). 'The Empty Protractor', *Mathematics Teaching* 253, pp.32-33 see also: **http://pinkmathematics.blogspot.com/ 2014/04/pie-charts-and-percentages-with-Smarties.html**

(7) If you want a coloured in Pie Chart you could also use Skittles and warm water: **youtube.com/watch?v=4FHbbc8v1Cs**

7   *Squares and 'Closest Rectangles'*

Jonathan Hall

Begin with a prompt:

> *Which has the greatest area, a square or a rectangle?*

No dimensions, encourage pupils to make up their own. Can we come up with a way of comparing them?

Let us introduce the idea of a 'closest rectangle'. We will define it, for this task, to mean the rectangle you create when you subtract one from the length and add it to the width of a square. For example, consider the area of a 5 × 5 cm square. The 'closest rectangle' to this square, with integer sides, is a 4 × 6 rectangle.

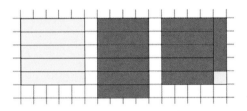

Compare the areas, what do you notice? Is the area of the rectangle one less than the square? Maybe this was a fluke, try it with a different-sized square. Does this always work?

Does the area of a square and its 'closest rectangle' always differ by one?

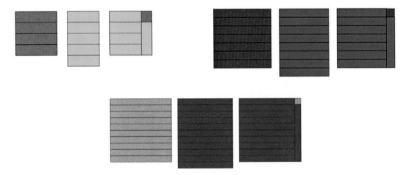

It certainly seems to be the case. Try a few more examples: 8 × 8 = 64 and 7 × 9 = 63, 4 × 4 = 16 and 3 × 5 = 15, 10 × 10 = 100 and 9 × 11 = 99.

Let us move away from building squares and use our new knowledge to calculate a much larger product.

What is 99 × 101?

Make a prediction. What do you think is the answer to 99 × 101? Why? See if you were right.

By now the pupils are generally keen to carry out a "boring" long multiplication problem, they have a reason for doing so. They are practising with a purpose.

"Ok, so how about 98 × 102?" I'm yet to meet a class that doesn't predict 9998 and the sense of disappointment is real when they arrive at 9996 using a procedural method. "Don't panic", I tell them, all is not lost. Let us specialise with smaller numbers and see if we can spot a different pattern.

Calculation	Answer	Difference from previous answer
5 × 5	25	
4 × 6	24	+1
3 × 7	21	+3
2 × 8	16	+5
1 × 9	9	+7
0 × 10	0	+9

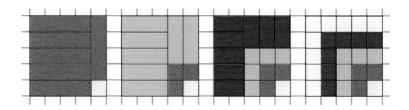

It is certainly no coincidence that the sum of consecutive odd integers from 1 to *n* is always a square number.

1	1
1 + 3	4
1 + 3 + 5	9
1 + 3 + 5 + 7	16
1 + 3 + 5 + 7 + 9	25

What if we did not know the length of the side of the square? Could we generalise the problem?

Take a square with side length x, its area will be x^2.

Consider the 'closest rectangle' with sides $x + 1$ and $x - 1$. Its area is

$$(x + 1)(x - 1) = x^2 - 1.$$

In other words, one less than the area of the square.

Calculation	Answer	Difference from x^2
$(x - 0)(x + 0)$	x^2	0
$(x - 1)(x + 1)$	$x^2 - 1$	1^2
$(x - 2)(x + 2)$	$x^2 - 4$	2^2
$(x - 3)(x + 3)$	$x^2 - 9$	3^2
$(x - 4)(x + 4)$	$x^2 - 16$	4^2
...	...	...
$(x - n)(x + n)$	$x^2 - n^2$	n^2

We have arrived at the difference of two squares:

$$(x - n)(x + n) = x^2 - n^2.$$

8   *Never Stop Learning*

Jemma Sherwood

I was in my third or fourth year of teaching when a newly-qualified colleague brought me a question like this

$$x(x + 2) = x(3x - 8).$$

She kept getting the solution $x = 5$, where the mark scheme said the solutions were $x = 0$ and $x = 5$, and she had reached a bit of a block. Her solution went like this:

$x(x + 2) = x(3x - 8)$ $x + 2 = 3x - 8$ $10 = 2x$ $5 = x.$	(divide both sides by x)

I asked her what happens if she starts by expanding the brackets and she very quickly got to a 'standard' quadratic equation which factorised to produce the missing solution.

We then chatted about why her initial move was an 'illegal' one and the discussion came to comparing this equation with something like $4(x + 2) = 4(3x - 8)$. What were the distinguishing features of each? Why is a particular 'technique' perfectly valid in one case but utterly invalid in another? We considered how one equation was linear and the other quadratic and how, by dividing both sides by x, she had reduced the order of the equation, consequently reducing the number of solutions.

The conversation has always stuck with me, partly because I had never explicitly thought about this idea until that point. I mean *really* thought about it. I knew she shouldn't have divided by the unknown, but I hadn't solidified *why* in my own head, and I hadn't done that because I'd always accepted it and had never been confronted with such an error before. The cognitive conflict my colleague experienced forced her to grasp an idea she had missed. The discussion around the problem forced me to categorise and to codify in a way I hadn't to that point.

There have been many times since then that the underlying idea – that of dividing by a variable, unknown, or constant – has cropped up in lessons. Take the following examples and ask yourself whether the stated division is valid and what the features of each statement are that lead you to your conclusion.

   A. We can divide both sides of $2x^2 + 4x - 10 = 0$ by 2 as a step towards solving the equation.

   B. We can divide both sides of $2x^2 + 4x = 0$ by x as a step towards solving the equation.

   C. We can divide both sides of $\sin^2 x + \cos^2 x \equiv 1$ by $\cos^2 x$ to get $\tan^2 x + 1 \equiv \sec^2 x$.

   D. We can divide both sides of $y = x^2 - 5x - 6$ by x to get $\frac{y}{x} = x - 5 - \frac{6}{x}$ and plot two identical curves.

   E. We can divide both sides of $\sin x = \cos x$ by $\cos x$ as a step towards solving the equation.

   F. We can divide both sides of $\sin x \cos x = \sin x$ by $\sin x$ as a step towards solving the equation.

Now ask yourself what principles explain the differences between each example and how you would communicate these principles to pupils at various stages of their mathematical development. There is much to be learnt here – about maths *and* about teaching it – from such a simple starting point.

In looking in more depth at a selection of problems, identifying what is the same and what is different, identifying what rules apply where, we take the procedures we learn in school and start to understand them on another level. I would contend that this process of increasing our understanding is never-ending, if we allow it to be.

Let's consider another example. At school I learnt to complete the square on a quadratic. Faced with something like $x^2 + 4x + 2$, I would dutifully halve the coefficient of x, write it in the squared bracket, square what I'd written and subtract from the constant term. I'd go through the process mechanically, but I *got* it too – I could be considered to be fluent. I knew that if I expanded $(x + 2)^2 - 2$ and collected like terms it would present as the original. No random, contextless algorithm here, just another way of writing the quadratic which helped me to solve an equation, or find the turning point, or recognise the transformation from x^2.

It wasn't until I was about ten years into teaching, however, that I spent some time looking at algebra tiles and area models. When I saw this, it blew my mind.

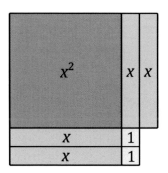

It was an *actual square*, with side length $(x + 2)$, missing two square units. And every quadratic could be arranged to an actual square, either with some square units too few, or too many. I had learned something new and it had improved my understanding of completing the square and quadratics generally.

For a long time after this, I believed my previous understanding had been insufficient – that I hadn't really understood completing the square before – but now I think 'insufficient' is the wrong word, because it implies linearity in understanding, or crossing a line from 'insufficient' to 'sufficient'. There is no such line, but there are connections and increasing depth and breadth of understanding. The realisation that came with seeing the area model added an extra dimension to what I knew, it drew yet another link to something else, and in doing so helped me to see more of the picture.

You see, learning is not linear, it's messy, and that's what makes the teacher's job a really difficult one. We take the domain of mathematics, let's picture it like this:

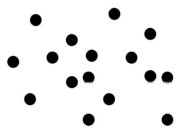

And we try to present it so that our pupils encounter a dot and connect it to the ones they already know about.

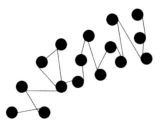

But the beauty about the never-ending nature of learning mathematics is that even when the domain of school mathematics is 'done' we can spend more time thinking about it and this happens:

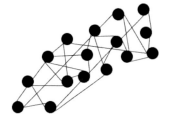

And then, more and more, *this* happens:

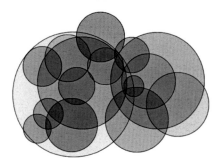

as the boundaries we'd created between topics and ideas start to break down.

The more we learn, the more we hold the domain of mathematics in a kind of tension between two competing ideas. On one end is my first example (equations, identities and division by constants and variables), where we gain clarity around concepts and details and can see the distinctions between types of question and types of construct. On the other end is my second example (completing the square algebraically or geometrically), where we understand how one mathematical idea can be viewed through the lens of another, where we *lose* distinctions between concepts and constructs or see them in the light of their superficiality.

This kind of learning, and the desire to pursue it, naturally feeds into our teaching. I see two major consequences of teacher as learner:

1. The more we understand the domain, the better we can communicate it. The better we communicate it, the more our pupils will learn.

2. The more we value and pursue learning for its own sake, the more we communicate to our pupils the value and the joy in the pursuit. The culture in our classroom starts with us, and to create a culture of learning, we must lead by example.

When we realise the power of teacher as learner, we understand our responsibility to chart a route for our pupils around the domain that helps *them* to make connections and grow their own web – or schema – of mathematics. The more we learn, the better the route we can map out. Understanding mathematics is not a "do you/don't you" binary, neither is it a continuum. It's more a broadly hierarchical, yet messy, web of connections, where each idea adds another dimension to what you know, how you conceptualise, and how you make sense of it all. And that makes teaching mathematics a joy, because you never stop learning.

9   *Actually Teach Mathematics*

Peter Mattock

If I could only tell you one thing about teaching mathematics it would be to make sure you are *actually teaching mathematics.* This of course seems obvious but there were many times in my earlier teaching career where, if I look back on them, I am not sure I was teaching mathematics. Rather I was teaching things like how to follow algorithms or different steps to memorise for solving different problem types.

Algorithms and problems are both important parts of mathematics, and studying them is a key part of learning mathematics. Even here though, in the language I have used, I have alluded to the point I hope to make – it is the study of the algorithms and problems that needs to occur and not just pupils learning to apply the algorithms or solve the problems. Of course, as part of the study of these things, pupils will learn to apply algorithms and will solve problems, but it is important not to stop there. Take, for example, the column addition algorithm:

$$
\begin{array}{ccc}
\mathsf{H} & \mathsf{T} & \mathsf{U} \\
1 & 1 & \\
2 & 4 & 9\,+ \\
1 & 6 & 8 \\
\hline
4 & 1 & 7 \\
\hline
\end{array}
$$

Pupils can be taught to add the ones, then the tens, then the hundreds (and so on), exchanging when necessary. But studying the algorithm yields so much more than just learning to apply it; we can reinforce and extend place value understanding (particularly if we then look at adding numbers in different bases). In addition (no pun intended), we can learn more about adding, and what it means to add numbers which use more than one symbol to create the numeral, which can then support when adding things like decimals, fractions or surds,

25.65 + 12.23	$5\frac{6}{11} + 2\frac{2}{11}$	$2\sqrt{3} + 5 + \sqrt{3} + 2$

   T U 1/10 1/100
   2 5.6 5
 + 1 2.2 3
   3 7.8 8
	
	   U 1/11
	   5 6
	   2 2
	   7 8
		
		   √3 U
		   2 5
		   1 2
		   3 7

as well as allowing pupils to use the algorithm flexibly, for example to sum the numbers 100002 + 30029.

$$
\begin{array}{ccccccc}
 & 1 & 0 & 0 & 0 & 0 & 2 \\
+ & & 3 & 0 & 0 & 2 & 9 \\
\hline
 & 1 & 3 & 0 & 0 & 3 & 1 \\
\end{array}
$$

The key idea here is that there is no real harm in this case in adding the hundred-thousands or ten-thousands values prior to the ones or tens: it doesn't really make a difference. But it does make much more sense to add the ones values prior to considering the tens value.

Studying the algorithm also allows pupils to consider situations where they can employ their reasoning abilities:

Solve the following (each letter represents a particular digit 0 to 9):

ABC + DEF = GHIJ

This is power of shifting the focus of study from a very narrow one of pupils applying given algorithms to the much wider one of pupils studying the algorithm themselves; pupils start to achieve some insight into the mathematical structure underlying the concepts from which the algorithm stems. It is teaching about this mathematical structure that I refer to when I say make sure you are actually teaching mathematics. For me, our goal as teachers of mathematics is to offer opportunities for pupils to gain and increase their awareness of mathematical structures, how we make sense of different mathematical concepts and how these concepts combine and overlap with each other. This might be through explicit teaching; through the use of representations and manipulatives:

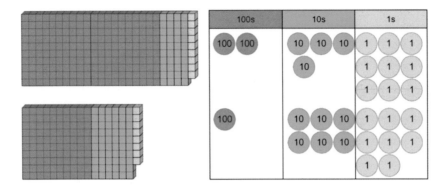

through the use of carefully structured sequences of questions:

Work out the following

a) $326 + 253$ b) $326 + 353$ c) $426 + 353$ d) $42 + 353$
e) $427 + 354$ f) $437 + 354$ g) $447 + 354$ h) $447 + 364$
i) $444 + 367$ j) $464 + 347$ k) $364 + 447$

or through the use of prompts that pupils can explore and develop:

Using each of the digits 1 to 6 how many different answers can you get by placing the digits in these boxes? What do you notice? How might you develop this further?

The decision for which of these approaches teachers will use rests with the teacher and will depend on their knowledge of the pupils, the culture they have developed and are trying to develop with the pupils around mathematics learning and the wider context in which they work (amongst other things).

The same is true of problem solving. Take for example the classic problem of finding a missing side in a right-angled triangle using Pythagoras' Theorem.

Find the value of y

Step 1: Identify the hypotenuse and the two legs.
12 is the hypotenuse, 8 and y are the two legs.

Step 2: Square each given side.
$8^2 = 64,$ $12^2 = 144.$

Step 3: If finding the hypotenuse, add the squares of each leg. If finding one of the legs, subtract the square of the other leg from the square of the hypotenuse.

144 – 64 = 80.

Step 4: Take the square root of your answer to step 3, this is the missing length

$y = \sqrt{80}$.

There are two issues here:

1) We are working in the realms of pupil memory; pupils will either remember these steps (and how to do the things within them) or they will forget. There are potentially things we can do to try and ensure more pupils are more likely to remember the steps, but that doesn't help with number 2;

2) These steps will only allow pupils to solve this particular type of problem. They won't help pupils to identify *when* to apply the steps, nor will they help in many of the other problem types that pupils may encounter that may or may not require Pythagoras' Theorem to help solve.

Again, the solution is to study the idea; to learn about Pythagoras' Theorem rather than learn to solve for missing sides in Pythagoras problems. We can offer opportunities for pupils to learn about Pythagoras' Theorem as a relationship between 3 sides in a right triangle, perhaps using dynamic geometry software to explore the relationship:

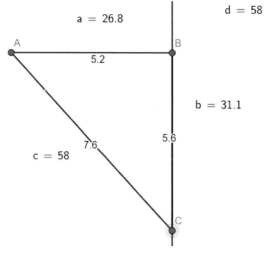

Maybe practical measurement:

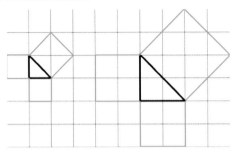

Or video demonstrations (like the excellent water demonstration at **www.youtube.com/watch?v=CAkMUdeB06o&t=9s** and/or formal geometric proof. Then, when pupils are comfortable with the relationship we can offer different problem types, including finding missing sides in triangles in different orientations:

Find the length of the side marked x.

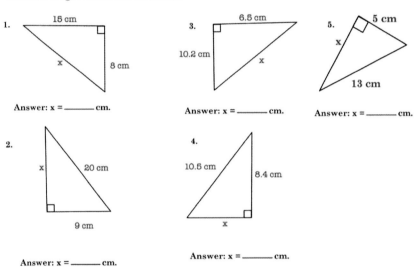

And then there are problems like those below:

Is the triangle below right-angled? Explain how you know.

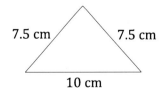

Does this triangle contain an obtuse angle? Explain how you know.

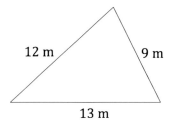

Will this square fit inside this circle without touching the edge? Show how you decide.

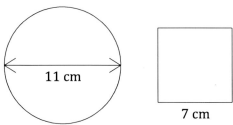

We don't explore these problem types in terms of trying to find and memorise steps to solving them, but rather to prompt (often with teacher support) an awareness of what Pythagoras' Theorem tells us about each situation, and therefore what the situations have in common.

Structure is inherent in all areas of maths. If we spend our time as teachers of mathematics ensuring that pupils are taught about, engage with and explore the structure underpinning the ideas they are working with, then we support the proper development of the foundations on which we can securely build algorithmic automaticity and fluent problem solving. So if I could tell you one thing about teaching mathematics, it would to ensure those foundations are in place; by all means teach kids how to apply algorithms and solve problems, but make sure it is in the wider context of the mathematical structures from which these algorithms and problems arise.

10   *Creativity, Fun and Geekiness*

Chris Smith

You know a wee bit about how infinity works. So it'll come as no surprise that there's only so much Maths that can be crammed into the official *finite* school curriculum.

Sensibly this includes fundamental operational skills (addition, subtraction, multiplication and division) and real life essentials (money calculations, working with time, basic fractions and percentages). There are also dozens of much loved staples for Maths teachers to drool over: who can resist simultaneous equations or hide their excitement when teaching Pythagoras' Theorem? Which of us hasn't relished showcasing the power of algebra to solve problems? How many times have you refereed a heated classroom debate over "quadratic formula" versus "completing the square"? And how lovely is it to watch the penny drop as a pupil finally "gets" prime numbers or masters factorising or appreciates trig identities?

Students are also legitimately invited to embark on a fascinating journey through Mathematical history as they explore concepts which were hugely controversial when they were first proposed. Negative numbers, irrational numbers and complex numbers were explosive, cutting edge ideas at one time, yet they're served up routinely to our kids. That should be kind of empowering to the young folk we teach, I reckon.

"And don't get me started on the titan battle between Newton and Leibniz" in the origins of calculus, Andrew Wiles' gripping triumph over Fermat's Last Theorem or the development of proofs from Euclid's classics through to computer-assisted Four Colour Theorem ... These tales aren't really tangents (except when they're teaching us about tangents) – these stories are important in communicating the human connection with our beautiful subject and undermining the myth that Maths is a dry subject where nothing exciting happens and where all the answers are already at the back of the textbook. Instead, we should broadcast that Maths has a rich, lively history and is a living, breathing endeavour with plenty of new discoveries still being made in our lifetime.

All of this makes it a real pleasure to teach Maths.

But take a peek beyond the course content and you'll spot lovely wee gems that have been edged out. Around the corner there are fascinating Mathematical curiosities, intriguing puzzles and entire branches of Mathematics which fascinate Maths teachers. Just look at the phenomenon that YouTube channel *Numberphile* has become (see Note 1). It demonstrates an appetite for learning about Maths even when that's entirely disconnected from the syllabus and number fans like us are lapping it up.

We don't limit ourselves to just those topics that are going to appear in the exam, so why limit *our students'* experience?

Maths and English share a privileged position in secondary school education. They're the non-negotiables, the compulsory course on the menu of subjects on offer. Inevitably, this means that there will be students in your class who adore Mathematics but equally others who have struggled with it previously and need a bit of convincing. Literal arm-twisting is frowned upon these days and may never have been the most effective strategy here. Of course, the way we handle Maths can help to win them over. But don't underestimate the impact of creativity, fun and geekiness. The time pressure of deadlines and final exams might loom and make it seem risky to shift the focus but the right event or project could captivate their imagination, create unforgettable memories and woo them to admit, even through gritted teeth, that they're invested in Maths now.

Temporarily abandoning the core curriculum to explore bizarre Mathematical trivia or to creatively celebrate stuff like PiDay or to coordinate Mathsy events is totally worth it! Sure, it takes time away from the exam-driven content but there's a payoff in the enthusiasm and motivation these antics generate. I've been grilled on this many times (including when Craig Barton interviewed me for his podcast: see Note 2) but as I've reflected on a decade and a half of teaching I'm utterly convinced that this approach, in tandem with passionate, sound teaching of the standard stuff, is a winning combination.

Generating a buzz in the Maths Department in the month of March has become part of the rhythm of our school year. The 14th of March (3.14 as our American pals write it) is known worldwide as PiDay. Here's a whistle-stop tour of ten very different, creative ways we've marked this event on the Mathematical calendar in the last decade.

2012: *Road to PiDay* **https://youtu.be/WaP2hOp6w14**	Graphing my car mileage each week for months - I reached the ePIc milestone of 31415 miles on PiDay (after driving round and round the school roundabout for that final mile).
2013: *Pi-MCA* **https://youtu.be/4FHuZaboPho**	Music, moustaches and inspiration stolen from the Village People. Lyrics written by our class. Winner of New York's Museum of Math's pi-related song contest for High Schools in 2015.
2014: *Pi in the Sky*	At the request of students to "share the Maths", I collected hundreds of students' favourite puzzles, selected a few to appear on postcards, attached them to helium balloons and we launched them into the sky, inviting recipients to complete the puzzles and post them back to us.
2015: *Pi-scrapers* **https://youtu.be/fvC8B-1ei10**	We hijacked the gym hall and created a skyline of pi-scrapers, each having the required number of stories which corresponded to the digits in pi, with the whole process timelapsed.
2016: *Pi-rotechnics*	We took slow exposure photographs of pupils tracing out digits using torches, iPhone lights and blowtorches (yes, actual blowtorches) to capture a few stunning images representing pi.

2017: *Pi-xel Art*	
	Hundreds and hundreds of staff and students had their photograph taken posing behind consecutive digits of pi. Each became a pi-xel in the final Mathsterpiece!
2018: *Pi-drotherapy*	Water-based PiDay shenanigans. We constructed a display using some plywood and 100 pipes. We filled each with coloured water so that all reds represent 3s, yellows represent 1s and so on.
2019: *Pi Hopes* https://youtu.be/4YOlO5apE88	Coordinating hundreds of mini Mathematicians into a precise line-up in typically awful Scottish weather was a real challenge but the aerial drone footage turned out pretty nifty.
2020: *TOpiARY* https://youtu.be/ClyybjOugeo	PiDay was a Sunday. I was at home and attempted to sculpt the hedge between my neighbour's garden and mine into the iconic pi logo. A future career in gardening isn't likely.
2021: *Eyes Pi Puzzle Hunt* https://youtu.be/AqlJa3ngrk8	I devised a monstrous 100-clue Puzzle Hunt around Kilmarnock. A few were pi-themed but the big reveal of the mystery route was the true pi tribute!

Plotting these PiDay stunts borders on an obsession for me personally but the lasting impression they have on students is what justifies their elaborate concoction! Years later, I'll bump into a former student in the supermarket or get a message on Facebook out of the blue and inevitably PiDay will get a mention. What strikes me is that it doesn't matter whether they're now pursuing a career in Mathematics or I simply helped that student scrape a "C" they needed or even if their school experience was fraught with discipline issues and learning setbacks. PiDay remains on their radar as a special catalyst which on some level inspired them and resulted in a degree of fondness for Maths.

Actually, I'd argue that PiDay has an impact and significance which stretches beyond our school community. These high profile, eye catching PiDay antics are eagerly anticipated and lapped up by the local newspaper who are always willing to share our Mathematical adventures with their readers. I am grateful for their support as this definitely helps create a positive perception of Maths as a subject which is useful, relevant, powerful but can also be creative, beautiful, joyous and for everyone! That's a powerful message and one worth reiterating whenever possible.

Of course, PiDay is just one of many strategies we use to enthuse students about Mathematics beyond the standard curriculum. They are also roped into Maths competitions, exposed to impromptu performances of Mathsy songs, challenged by fiendish puzzles, introduced to bizarre number facts, mesmerised by Maths-powered magic, treated to visits from inspirational Maths communicators and invited to our legendary Maths Camps. Yes, Maths Camps. When pandemics aren't wreaking havoc with our plans, we have over 100 campers traipsing off for a weekend of Mathematical revision and geeky entertainment. It's become an institution, the stuff of legends, with kids signing up in their droves for this unforgettable residential. When the 2020 edition was cruelly snatched from us by COVID days before we were due to head off, the disappointment spread through the school like, well, a virus. There were actual tears.

This is just a snapshot of the kind of commitment, motivation and affection that's nurtured in a place where a love of Maths is normalised and where that passion and enthusiasm doesn't end with the official learning objectives forced on us by curriculum designers and exam authorities.

It's bold to take the decision to allow yourself a breather from the relentless march through the course to excitedly explain something you've recently learned, or to plan together a geeky PiDay celebration, to create and perform a Mathematical song, or to collaborate on an unlikely project (Note 3).

But it might just provide that spark of inspiration that encourages the class roaster to be a bit more cooperative or cause a talented student to pursue Maths as a career. There's no guarantee but it might even begin a shift towards a school where the Maths corridor is the place to be, where senior students sign up *en masse* for Advanced Higher, where the prospect of one day attending Maths Camp is a dream of hundreds of pupils and where the question "what are we doing for PiDay this year, sir?" is heard months before the big day.

Mission accomplished.

Notes

(1) www.youtube.com/user/numberphile
(2) www.mrbartonmaths.com/blog/chris-smith-injecting-fun-into-lessons-resources-pi-day-revision-days/
(3) www.tes.com/news/vanilla-ice-unlikeliest-education-gurus

11   *If I Could Show You One Puzzle*

Catriona Agg

If I could show you one puzzle, it would be this one.

Two squares sit on the hypotenuse of a right-angled triangle. What's the angle between the pink line and the base?

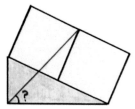

There are lots of things I like about this puzzle, but the first is its **simplicity**. There are just three shapes here, and two of them are the same! None of the shapes are difficult to draw, and it's easy to see how they fit together. A quick glance is enough to take this puzzle in.

If you have squared paper, it's not too hard to construct the tilted squares accurately. But at this point you might start to notice the second thing I like about this puzzle, which is that **it doesn't seem to give you enough information**. What dimensions are we supposed to use for the right-angled triangle? Surely the tilt of the hypotenuse is crucial, when the question asks us for an angle?

Here are a few of my attempts to press on regardless, with a variety of different scale drawings. Incredibly, it really does seem like the details of the right-angled triangle don't really matter. The angle is always the same! In fact, the third thing I like about this puzzle is that **although features of the diagram can change, the answer is invariant**.

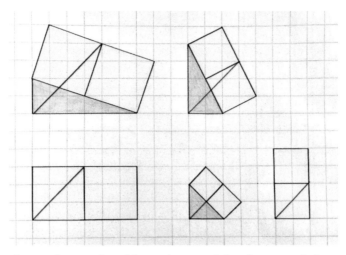

You might not be comfortable with two of the diagrams I drew in the bottom row. They're the extreme cases, where either the height or width of the triangle is zero – and so you could argue that the triangle is no longer there! But I drew them because the fourth thing I like about this puzzle is that **there's a cheat's solution**. If we believe that the answer doesn't depend on the shape of the triangle, why not pick a shape that's easy to reason about? It's much easier to argue that the angle is 45° from any of the three diagrams in the bottom row than in a more general case. However, the cheat's solution always relies on the assumption that an invariant answer exists, so you might not feel it's very satisfactory. Fear not though, because the thing I really love about this puzzle is that **there are multiple ways to solve it**.

There are two solutions that I particularly love. Both work no matter what dimensions you choose for the right-angled triangle. And both rely on seeing the diagram in the puzzle as part of a bigger picture. Here is a diagram showing the main idea in each. Can you complete the arguments?

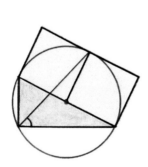
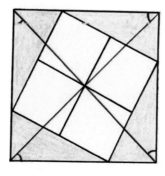

12   *Easy as a, b, c*

Jo Sibley

I'm a convert to mini-whiteboards in the classroom, for the immediate low-stakes feedback, for spotting notation and vocab issues, for voting and so much more. One of my favourite uses for mini-whiteboards is for example generation. Giving the students the power to choose the numbers that will appear in an example gives it authenticity. Not only does this new method they're learning work for the numbers the teacher has chosen, it also works for the versions they design themselves (until it doesn't, more on that story later).

I probably use 'Easy as *a*, *b*, *c*' as a lesson starter most commonly, but it has also generated whole lessons, as we explore the ramifications of a particular combination of selected values. But I'm getting ahead of myself. What's the basic technique? Classes I've worked with for a couple of weeks will quickly have picked up what I'm looking for if they walk into a lesson and a trigger something like this is on the board:

Choose *a*, *b*, *c*, *d*; integers between -6 and 6.

Sometimes the prompt specifics are different: I might only want positives, sometimes I'll allow non-integers, or only multiples of six or only primes. There's usually some discussion to be had and I welcome that, especially in the first few weeks. The students must write their four numbers down and there's trust inherent that they don't then change them – or that they at least tell me if they do, along with the all-important WHY.

The kid who challenges me on whether zero is an integer or if it's positive or negative, trying to catch me out, gets bonus praise. My convention, which the students usually check on quickly, is that their choices don't need to be distinct, but they learn fast that choosing four zeroes makes for really dull examples – unless it doesn't! – More on that story later...

Here are three cases of how I might use the idea.

Case 1. Consolidating fractions understanding

The school I've spent most of my career in draws students from a huge number of feeder schools and, until Mastery became more widespread in our local feeders, the first time we met fractions in Year 7 always felt like trying to nail jelly to the ceiling. I needed a way to almost start completely afresh with fractions, without alienating those who had already had fractions up to their eyeballs and wanted to crack on with more interesting stuff. I would start with the prompt from above:

Choose a, b, c, d; integers between -6 and 6.

Once they'd got their four values written down (I'm hammering the vocab: constant, value, integer etc, we make sure nobody's taking these for granted), I say,

"Write these fractions on your whiteboard, replacing the constants with your values:
$$\frac{a}{b} \qquad \frac{c}{d}$$
"Don't do anything else with them yet!

"Right, hold up your board if one or both of your fractions ..." and then I choose a category (not necessarily in this order, I'll be peeking over shoulders to see what might present an interesting answer – yay for mini-whiteboards making this easy):

- Could be simplified
- Is equal to an integer
- Has the same value as ½ or -½
- Is equal to zero
- Is equal to one
- Is undefined

(At least one of the last three should have our Four-Zeroes friend hopping up and down, and if they're really on the case, possibly all three!)

'Is undefined' is a big idea for Year 7, isn't it? I guess you could leave that one out and fix the initial call to action to exclude zero but, personally, that's where part of the magic of this technique lies, we're just opening students up slightly to the possibility that they can actually generate example that don't work – that there's a bit more to this maths lark than just the questions in the book with the answers in the back – and that's no bad thing when you're working with Fractions-Aaaaaagh Kid alongside Fractions-This-Is-Baby-Stuff Kid.

At some point, I'll ask if there are any fractions which don't fit any of the categories already listed: students who offer a top-heavy fraction at this point get a big smile and we talk about how a mixed number like $1\frac{2}{3}$ is hard to work with, and its top-heavy sibling $\frac{5}{3}$ is much more useful to mathematicians but less likely to appear 'in the wild', as it were.

One of the bits I like best about this is the discussion that arises from examples where there is a negative in the denominator. Is that ok? Does that count as 'not simplified'? I would argue that that's a fraction that can be simplified, and gently prod my thinkers towards asking why it's not ok to have a negative in the denominator. I think this gets skimmed sometimes – 'we just do', 'that's the way it's done' etc. Explaining *now* that not having negatives in the denominator is a convention, and a convention is usually a means by which mathematicians simplify the way they talk to each other, so they can all use the same process for a calculation, will mean that when you're trying to justify the 'yes, but why' of rationalising the denominator of a fraction when you're working on surds, you'll at least have a precedent to refer to. It helps demystify the process and moves students towards the understanding that while there's often not just one way of doing something in maths (a new fact for many Year 7 students), there is often a conventional way of doing it, which helps mathematicians with experience to work more efficiently.

I could happily extend this process to fill a full hour, depending on results of the first ten minutes. We might collectively create a Venn diagram of types of fractions generated, or go on a side quest about the numbers which are more likely to generate fractions that can be simplified and why.

If the group are looking happy and confident, I'll ask them to simplify their choices as far as possible (at this point Four-Zeroes Kid is going to need to make alternative choices, sorry) and then we can try multiplying and dividing our fraction pairs. It's a personal preference here to start with multiplying and dividing. I like to get this clear before the whole common denominator business clouds everything, and a real bugbear of mine is leaving division right to the end — pair it up with multiplication, don't split up the family.

Again, we have the chance here to do some classification:

"Are you multiplying/dividing:

- A fraction by an integer or vice versa?
- A fraction by a fraction?
- Something else?

"What are the differences in the process? What's the same?"

And then onward to addition and subtraction …

Case 2. Quadratics fundamentals

In the fractions example, it's nice to include all the stuff that 'doesn't work' alongside those that do, because the discussion generated is valuable for separating the students free-formed understanding of what works from the conventions that we accidentally impose by our choice of initial examples. Working with quadratics, we have to be a bit shrewder. If we were to set this trigger:

Choose a, b, c; integers between -6 and 6

and then: "Write down the equation $ax^2 + bx + c = 0$ and then solve it to find x"

… with a KS4 class, we're going to hit disaster fast. We *could* loudly consider all the versions that don't work, and I guess that would be interesting given plenty of time and high levels of student enthusiasm, but I suspect that quadratics are a risky place to play this game and we may end up investigating a rabbit hole we don't really want to spend any time down. (It would be an awesome rabbit hole for A level students to tumble into, of course.)

There's another risk in using this technique for quadratics and this time it's convention working against us; a, b and c have specific significance in quadratics and we really don't want to cause unnecessary confusion by doubling up on their use. Here's one of the ways I'd use this, then:

Choose α, β; integers between -10 and 10.

"Write them down *without showing anyone* and turn over your whiteboard …" (We hope at this point your boards are double sided, if not, students can write α and β in their books.)

"Write down the values of $\alpha + \beta$ and $\alpha\beta$ on your whiteboard and hold them up."

At this point, depending on the experience and capacity for keeping a secret in the group, I'll either ask the students to 'solve' their neighbour's puzzle to find their α and β or I'll pick examples myself.

Things I like to draw out (I ask the students to write down 'noticings' as we go along):

- The effect of the sign of α and β on the sign of their product
- The effect of the sign of α and β on the sign of their sum
- What happens if α or β is 1?
- What if α or β is 0?
- What if $\alpha = \beta$?
- What if $\alpha = -\beta$?

When we've squeezed all the juice out of this, we compile a summary of noticings which we'll refer back to in the following activities on expanding and factorising quadratics.

Later, we could still make use of that first disaster scenario with a tiny adaptation - with graphing software ready to go, we change the task to:

Choose a, b, c; integers between -6 and 6,

then: "Write down the function $f(x) = ax^2 + bx + c$, replacing a, b and c with your chosen values. Can you suggest what the graph of $y = f(x)$ might look like?"

Setting up sliders ahead of time for a, b and c within the range you'll use, and starting with $a = 1, b = 0$ and $c = 0$, you can then choose responses from students to gradually ramp up the difficulty and emphasise whatever you choose to emphasise (pro-tip: You may want to fix a at 1 or -1 at least to start, but take care to keep the trigger consistent with b being the coefficient of x and c being the constant).

Case 3. Heist questions

All good heist movies set out the idea that when planning a heist, you and your gang must meticulously cover all the possible eventualities you are aware of in your scheme but also be prepared for the unexpected. Heist questions are based on this – the students must (collaborate to) plan how to answer a question before they have all the information so that, on the day of the robbery, when they do have all the information they can solve the question in a flash. It's the Easy as a, b, c routine but in reverse, with a trigger such as:

"I have chosen a, b, c, d; integers between -6 and 6. (In your pairs/teams), make a plan to find the pair of values for x and y which work in both these equations simultaneously:

$$y = ax + b$$
$$cx + dy = 24.$$

"You have five minutes to make your plan."

(I'm a bit of a stickler for getting students familiar with both implicit and explicit formulae, but obviously that second formula could be adjusted to:

$$y = cx + d$$

... to simplify things a bit.)

When it looks like most have a heinous plot in place, I'll reveal my values and depending on how kind I'm feeling, I'll give them a head start by putting the values into the formulae for them:

"Your values are: $a = 3, b = -5, c = 4, d = 3$ so you're solving:

$$y = 3x - 5$$
$$4x + 3y = 24.$$

Teams who locate graphing software on their phones and set up the two equations with sliders during the planning phase clearly have the potential to be criminal masterminds in the making and should be encouraged enthusiastically.

I like this approach because it fosters enormously important transferable skills. Listening in to student conversations in the planning phase is fascinating: students who say "I hope one of the values turns out to be zero", and have additional short-cut strategies for that type of eventuality are showing good skills of flexibility. Being able to work through the stages of a task in general terms, without knowing the specifics of that problem, is useful when practising proof and when problem solving more widely.

Two more of my favourite heist questions, both based on curve sketching:

"You have five minutes to make a plan to sketch $y = ax^3 + bx^2 + cx + d$ and find the place(s) where it crosses the x-axis ...

" Ok, you have 30 seconds: $a = 1, b = 0, c = 4, d = 0$ GO!"

And my all-time favourite:

"You have five minutes to make a plan to sketch

$$y = \frac{a}{(x-b)(x-c)}$$

and find the place(s) where it crosses the x-axis ...

" Ok, you have 30 seconds: $a = 3, b = 2, c = -2, d = 0$ GO!"

(You may notice a predilection for difference of two squares examples. I put my hands up to that.)

And there we have it, Easy as a, b, c. Now to get rid of the earworm ...

13   *Good with Being 'Good'*

Nate Evans

To quote the Disney masterpiece, *Inside Out*:

> *"Do you ever look at someone and wonder what is going on inside their head?"*

I know that I have. Mainly during my teacher training watching experienced teachers soar through a lesson without breaking sweat. Something that I did a lot during my training year. Thank goodness for sweat-proof undershirts.

I digress ... What I wanted to share was the thoughts of every new teacher. What are they thinking during their lessons? Imagine the part in *Inside Out* when Joy is gone and all of the other feelings take over. It's a bit like that. So, now for something a bit different. A few moments of escapism from real life and into the mind of a new teacher. I hope that by doing that anyone with similar thoughts will have the feeling of relief that they are not alone.

First, we need to set the scene. You are a new teacher, and you've spent a **L-O-N-G** time creating what you see as the *perfect* lesson. You've planned for every misconception that you could imagine, you've collated, printed and cut some brilliant resources. You know where there could be some behaviour issues, you feel like you've got perfect timings because you've laid out minute by minute exactly what you are doing in the lesson (possibly even second by second) and that's how prepped you are. Though you definitely shouldn't have stayed up until, *"stop yawning"*, **9:30 pm** to do this, you night owl.

The class arrive *three whole minutes* late because their previous lesson was on the other side of school to where you are but it's okay, you've accounted for time at the start and time at the end for this shocking lateness. The starter activity is on the board ready, you're stood at the door tapping your watch and ushering them into the room in true sheepdog fashion. The books are laid out on their desks, the timer has started and we're off!

Five minutes in and it's all going really well, you're pacing around the room observing how everyone is getting on when a chuckle comes from the other side of the room – "*are they not focused?*" - A glare is directed towards them and they put their heads down and get on with the work again. An absolute win for challenging low-level behaviour issues.

The pacing continues – "*have they seriously only done three questions in this time?*" - after a vocalised reminder of how many questions that there actually **are** and a couple of extra minutes of work it's time for pens down and start of feedback. Those added couple of minutes do set off the internal panic that you are now a full two minutes behind on that meticulous plan that you made – "*why are you sweating? It's 2° outside*" – it'll be fine.

The responses from the starter didn't go *exactly* how the metaphorical dream board displayed as you took a question from the S-L-O-W-E-S-T talker in the classroom and in your 'two-minutes-behind' fuelled panic your brain stopped computing completely.

"*...what did they say? Were they words? Why is everyone staring at me? Oh wait ... I'm the teacher, that's why.*"

"Great question, I'm actually going to open this up to the room, who thinks they know the answer to this?" – A sea of hands rise up from the depths of the classroom and you select the most enthusiastic person – "*You. Are. A. Genius.*"

*Ah, where did those 8 minutes go?**

You get them to open their books and write today's date and title.

"*What do you mean black pen or green pen? Why would you write in green for your main piece of work?*"

"Black pen please and remember to underline with a pencil and a ruler to keep that presentation tip-top". They do that pretty quickly after that push for haste with your menacing countdown that didn't involve a single "... and a half" or "... and three quarters" – you know and they know that you mean business.

Now to the main part of the lesson, the information that will come from your mouth will be arguably the single greatest pieces of information these children have ever heard.

Probably...

You're in the flow, you have different coloured pens to show different stages of the process and you're pointing out common mistakes left, right and centre. Your board work is exceptional and you can see a nod of understanding in the distance from the back-right corner of the room so you carry on – *"stop turning towards the board, remember the training and face the audience – how do people's shoulders turn that way? You look like a teapot"* – you've given the example but their faces don't seem to be smiling as much as yours, it's best to ask if they understand.

Right, so that's a big fat no then. Not a single person said they understood a word of what you were saying, not even the phantom nodder at the back of the room – *"was that your imagination playing with you?"* – It's okay though, you'd planned for this, you had another example up your sleeve. You leave the previous example on the board, mainly because you don't want to rub it out as it was beautiful and you may leave it there for all eternity.

"So now we're going to do a bit of a "we do" activity, we're going to do it together following the steps from the previous example" - *these lollipop sticks are going to come in handy now* - you keep repeating the rule in your head:

> **Question, give thinking time, then say the name.**
> **Question, give thinking time, then say the name.**

"David, what is the next step?" – *"...why are you like this?"*

The 'we do' activity shows that they do know what they're doing and maybe just didn't want to put their hands up to say they get the work – *"probably won't do it that way next time"* – they're prepped and ready to go, the precious time you spent last night trimming down worksheets and making them perfectly sized is going to pay off now.

Ah.

The sheets do that really annoying thing where they're really hard to separate after you've trimmed the edges using the squeaky guillotine. "Take one and pass them along, once you've got your sheet you can start straight away on your own to practise what we've just done for yourself."

"Why are they saying they don't have a sheet? There were exactly 30 sheets? Of course you didn't print off spares, the planet is dying and you can definitely count to 30 ... well, you can probably count to 30... Hmm, can you actually count to 30?"

"Rub your sheets together everyone, let's find the missing ones." – why you said it like that you have no idea, you're now over-thinking everything you are saying because three children gave you a bit of a strange look since you shouted "rub your sheets" directly into their ears – *"judgemental much?"* – No joy though.

You zone out for what feels like a lifetime to figure out your next move – **how can you not count? How on earth is it possible to not print off enough worksheets? What are you going to do? Do you get them to share? What if they start talking and that sets everyone off? Why have they started talking? Give me a moment to think ... Maybe I should get back to the class now** – longest 2.6 seconds of your life.

"Right everyone, one between two it is." The phantom nodder gives you the nod of approval. Probably. You don't actually know. It could be a mirage. You take that as being the decision-making process finished, you explain the change and collect the extra sheets from each desk to pass them on to the bunch of children who thought they were getting away with doing no work. The evil teacher strikes again.

The monitoring continues, a few glares here and there but overall, they're doing the work that you've set and they've only needed to ask about which questions they are doing 43 times. Crisis averted.

A hand shoots up. "Can we set off to our next lesson please?"
"Next lesson? What do you ... Wait, is that clock fast?*
Military operation incoming. "Books to the back, sheets to the front, let's get these books in nice piles and let's move out class. Go, go, go." – *"Crikey David, you can't finish your work, what do you think this is – school? Let's get moving."*
Calm ensues and they leave for their next lesson with 8.2 seconds to spare.

"Thank you" whispers the very last child on their way out, it was from one of the children you glared at during the starter. That right there made everything worthwhile.

End scene. You're back in the room.

You will have lessons that feel like absolutely everything is going wrong. You will feel frustrated that you spent so long planning for what feels like a far from perfect session. But, here's the thing, that was <u>not</u> a bad lesson just because it didn't match your meticulous plan. There's no such thing as a bad lesson as long as the children take something worthwhile away with them that day.

If you take anything away from this story let it be this; this was a lesson where on-the-spot thinking has been done. This was a lesson where misconceptions were addressed, despite it taking up 5 extra minutes. This was a lesson with engaging teaching and optimal time to work on the task. This was a good lesson.

In my first lesson as an NQT I think I tried to read the word 'the' and the more I looked at it, the weirder it looked.
THE, *the*, T-H-E, tee-hee.

That's it, a heart-warming, humorous, yet honest look into a lesson as a new teacher and the thoughts that you will face at one time or another because it's natural to be ever-critical but if I could only tell you one thing: To fall in love with teaching you need to be "good with being good" and to not get on top of yourself. You're doing a cracking job.

... Oh, and one more thing:

The printer can smell your fear. It will always need its toner changing, the paper will jam or will be low on ink *exactly* when you need to use it. Nobody knows how to solve this so you are not alone. I like to believe that there are printer-elves that fix printers precisely when you don't need them because they have an issue with you for one reason or another. It was probably that time you printed in colour instead of black and white ... You monster.

14   *Surprise*

Sudeep Gokarakonda

Surprises can capture our attention, spark our curiosity, and make us question how well we understand something. Surprises are often delightful. For these reasons, surprises can be very memorable. Let's start with a handful of problems.

Problem 1: Deck of cards

This problem is from Alex Bellos' *Did you solve it?* column in *The Guardian*.

> Your friend chooses at random a card from a standard deck of 52 cards, and keeps this card concealed. You have to guess which of the 52 cards it is.
>
> Before your guess, you can ask your friend one of the following three questions:
>
> - is the card red?
> - is the card a face card? (Jack, Queen or King)
> - is the card the ace of spades?
>
> Your friend will answer truthfully. What question would you ask that gives you the best chance of guessing the correct card?

Problem 2: Whisky and water

I first came across this kind of problem in *Why Do Buses Come in Threes?* by Rob Eastaway and Jeremy Wyndham.

> You have a half-full glass of neat whisky, and another glass containing some water. You pour some water into the whisky glass, and then pour some of this mixture back into the water glass so that the whisky glass is exactly half-full again. Is there now more water in the whisky glass than there is whisky in the water glass?

Problem 3: Shaded triangle

Here is a question that I shared on Twitter:

ABCD is a square. *AC* is 12 cm. What is the area of Δ*ABC?*

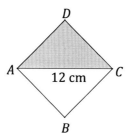

Problem 4: Overlapping rectangles

Here is another problem I tweeted in 2019.

Find the shaded area.

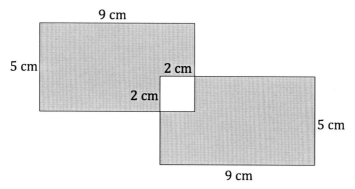

The answers to these problems are revealed in the following section, so make sure you've had a go at them for yourself first. Of course, you may have come across one or more of them before, in which case they may no longer surprise you. That fact notwithstanding, intended surprises are more likely to be surprises if they aren't signposted as such. I realise I have done precisely the opposite in this chapter! The title and introduction will have primed you to expect surprises. Therefore, the answers here may feel slightly less remarkable than they would have otherwise.

My takeaways from these problems

(1) Unexpected solutions can increase engagement

I came across the first problem, *Deck of cards*, on Twitter in June 2021. Beyond a familiarity with the standard deck of cards, the problem requires no knowledge beyond GCSE maths. This problem is rewarding to ponder not because of any inherent difficulty, but because of its surprising solution. No matter which of the three questions you ask, you can give yourself a 1/26 chance of being correct. In other words, there is no one question that gives you the best chance. This was certainly not obvious to me before I attempted the question. As I started working it out, I saw why the solution is as it is, but the sense of surprise lingers nonetheless.

Rob Eastaway, contrasting *puzzles* against *maths questions* in *Mathematics in School* from January 2021, suggests that "if you want to engage more of your students … the problems you pose to them need to be more puzzly." He goes on to say that the enjoyment sometimes "comes in discovering an unexpected solution, rather than in the problem or working out." The great Don Steward clearly appreciated this – whilst the *working out* is where you'll experience the highlights of many of his tasks, there are some more "routine" tasks in which the final solution itself (or a pattern amongst the solutions), is where the greater delight lies.

The second problem, *Whisky and water*, is in a sense similar to the first problem. The delight here is in the solution itself: the amounts of water in the whisky glass and whisky in the water glass are *equal*.

(2) Problems with simple solutions remind us to take a step back

Consider the third problem, *Shaded triangle*. The answer itself is *not* surprising, nor is it difficult to obtain for any teacher or older secondary student. Pose this problem to a secondary student or even an adult, and you'll find many end up using Pythagoras *en route* to obtaining the correct answer, which is 36 cm². On the other hand, younger students often answer this much more quickly by spotting that the shaded triangle has a base of 12 cm and a height of 6 cm. Not knowing the formula for the area of a triangle doesn't even prove to be a barrier; they readily see that the triangle can be halved and rearranged into a square of side 6 cm.

Students that have learned more advanced techniques can sometimes be tempted to use such techniques unthinkingly. There are times when we want students to develop automaticity in some sense, but we never want them to just use the first technique that comes to mind without pausing for thought. Finding the area using knowledge of Pythagoras and surds is likely to take longer *and* be more likely to lead to errors. Exposure to problems that can realistically be solved using both elementary and more advanced techniques can help remind students that it is worth taking a step back before diving into a problem.

(3) The hypercorrection effect is powerful

The concept of surprise crops up in educational research—notably in relation to the *hypercorrection effect*. Craig Barton describes this as the effect that arises "when students have given a response to a question which they feel confident is correct, but then discover that their response is wrong." The resulting sense of surprise or shock leads to an increased likelihood of the students remembering the correction, "thus improving long-term learning of the idea or concept."

Consider *Overlapping rectangles*, the fourth of the problems posed above. This is a favourite of mine, and it makes for a nice link to intersections of sets. When primed with the knowledge that the answer is surprising, people do tend to get the correct answer, which is 82 cm². On the other hand, when presented with the problem "cold", many students—and even teachers—obtain 86 cm². The error here is a classic: they add the areas of the large rectangles and subtract the area of the overlap. Months after exposing students to this problem, I've often set them a visually very different but structurally similar problem. With no prompting from me, the majority not only avoid falling into the trap, but they explicitly mention how this is like "that problem with the rectangles."

A cousin of the hypercorrection effect?

Finally, I'd like to explore something similar to – but not the same as – the hypercorrection effect. The hypercorrection effect in essence is finding that *errors* committed with higher confidence are easier to correct. I've emphasised *errors* here because I'd like to suggest, admittedly from my own experiences, that a similar effect can be observed even when students answer problems *correctly*, but inefficiently.

Consider the following problem, which I'll call *Billy's differences*:

> Billy is supposed to work out 91– 34 but he misreads this and works out 91– 43 instead. What is the difference between Billy's answer and the answer he should have got?

This is a type of problem I've used with many primary students. Very often, students will perform three calculations *en route* to the correct answer: 91 – 34 = 57, 91 – 43 = 48, and 57 – 48 = 9, which is the difference being sought.

Of course, a more efficient way to obtain this answer would be to simply calculate 43 – 34. As teachers, we would want students to be able to spot this more efficient route *and to have a sense of why this works*. We could go about this by using a number line, and perhaps explicitly presenting the question above alongside a similar one in an example-problem pair. Doing so would probably lead to a greater immediate success, i.e. a greater proportion of students would answer the question using the more efficient method. This would largely remove the element of surprise, however.

An alternative approach would be to let students attempt the question *without* priming them beforehand. In this scenario, students may get the question correct but nonetheless experience something akin to hypercorrection when they discover that they missed a shortcut.

Many teachers oppose giving students problems that they cannot yet access, often with good reason. Here, however, the subtraction problem is perfectly accessible, assuming students know how to subtract. For the right group of students, it just may be that their sense of subtraction is not quite mature enough to spot the shortcut for themselves, but mature enough to appreciate it with a little help from the teacher.

This problem is similar to the *Shaded triangle* problem in that there are clear efficient and inefficient ways to go about solving it. In the shaded triangle problem, students typically use the inefficient way (involving Pythagoras) not because they lack knowledge required to use a more efficient method, but because they've dived into the problem without considering that there might be a simpler, more efficient route to take. On the other hand, in the problem of *Billy's differences*, students typically use an inefficient method because they lack the understanding to use the more efficient method.

In such situations, I would suggest that allowing students to work through their less efficient methods before exploring more efficient methods can surprise the students – in a good way – by making the important "sense-making" moments in lessons a bit more memorable.

15   *Everybody's Free*

Kyle Evans

Everybody's free (to use mini-whiteboards)
with apologies to Mary Schmich, Baz Luhrmann & Edsger Dijkstra

Ladies, gentlemen, and everyone
The class of '21
Use whiteboards
If I could offer you only one tip for the future, mini whiteboards would be
it
The learning benefits of mini whiteboards have been proved in various
studies by education experts
Whereas the rest of my advice has no basis more reliable
Than my own meandering experience
I will dispense this advice now

Enjoy the power and beauty of your NQT year
Oh never mind
You will not understand the power and beauty of your NQT year until it's
faded
But trust me, in 5 years you'll look back at your timetable
And recall in a way you can't grasp now
How much possibility lay before you and how many free periods you
really had

You are not as tired as you imagine

Don't worry about the future
Or worry, but know that worrying
Is as effective as trying to solve an algebra equation by chewing bubble
gum
(And obviously don't try to solve an algebra equation by chewing bubble
gum)
The real troubles in your life
Are apt to be things that never crossed your worried mind
The kind that blindsides you at 4 p.m. on some idle Tuesday
Such as realising, from nowhere, that every odd number has an 'e' in it

Do one worked example every day that scares you

Shortcuts are fine, as long as you explain why they work
Remember: every time you do 'keep flip change' without explaining why it
works, a fairy dies

Don't be reckless with other people's glue sticks
Don't put up with people who are reckless with yours

Floss (but don't let your students do it in class)

Don't be too critical of the enthusiastic young NQT with their new
initiatives
Or the tired 30-year veteran with their arms crossed through CPD
You were probably the former once
And you might yet be the latter

Remember the good line managers you've had, forget the bad ones
If you succeed in doing this, tell me how
Keep your old thank you cards from year 11s
Throw away your old detention slips

Stretch (by scale factor 2, parallel to the y-axis)

The most interesting people I know
Didn't know at 22 what they wanted to do with their lives
Some of the most interesting 40-year-olds I know still don't
So don't feel guilty if you don't know what you want to do with your life
(Unless you're education secretary)

Be kind to your LSAs
You'll miss them when they're gone

Maybe you'll go part-time, maybe you won't
Maybe you'll move into SLT, maybe you won't
Maybe you'll quit teaching at 40
Maybe you'll dance the Funky Chicken on your 50th leavers' prom at the
same school
Whatever you do, don't congratulate yourself too much
Or berate yourself either
Your choices are half chance, so are everybody else's
(Please note this is approximately half chance: just because an event has
two outcomes does not necessarily make them equally likely)

Enjoy your calculator, use it every way you can
Don't be afraid of it or what other people think of it

It's the greatest instrument you'll ever own

Dance, even if you have nowhere to do it but your own classroom

Read the directions even if you don't follow them
Actually, don't bother
There's always a student that can show you what to do

Don't pick fights on edutwitter, it will only make you feel dirty

Get to know the department veteran, you never know when they'll be
retired for good
Be nice to your siblings, they're your best link to your past
Unless your sister keeps tagging you in on those trolling facebook emoji
BODMAS questions
Understand that teaching colleagues come and go
But a precious few will hold on

Work hard to bridge the gaps in geography and lifestyle
(Especially if you're literally bridging a gap in the geography department
In which case make sure you get back to maths ASAP)
For as the older you get
The more you need the people you knew when you were young

Teach bottom set year 10 once, but leave before it makes you hard
Teach year 13 further maths once, but leave before it makes you soft

Accept certain inalienable truths
Year 9s will be bored and hormonal, kids will think $(x + y)^2$ means
$x^2 + y^2$
You too will get old
And when you do, you'll fantasize that when you were young
Year 9s behaved and kids remembered the $2xy$

Use all the great technology you can find
But to paraphrase Fun Boy Three & Bananarama:
"It's more what you say than the way that you say it"
After all, astronomy is not the study of telescopes

Don't mess too much with your wall displays
Or the kids will spend more time looking at the pretty colours than the
important thing (you)

Be careful whose advice you buy but be patient with those who supply it

73

Advice is a form of nostalgia
Dispensing it is a way of fishing the past from the rubbish bin
Wiping it off
Painting over the ugly parts
And recycling it for more than it's worth

But trust me on the whiteboards

16   *Understanding and Solving Problems*

Stephen Cavadino

Mathematics is a discipline that is often misunderstood. You hear people say repeatedly that there is always a right or wrong answer. Often this is the case, but there is very rarely a single correct *solution*. When people characterise mathematics in this manner, they put it into a box. They write it off as a subject that is nothing more than a series of algorithms to be learned and practised until they can be recreated. This is not maths. Maths is a beautiful subject, one that is full of ideas and inspirations. Maths is an art, and it is full of creativity. Ian Stewart sums it up well in the introduction to his book *From Here to Infinity* when he says: "Mathematics is not about symbols and calculations, these are tools of the trade ... Mathematics is about ideas ... It is about how ideas relate to each other ... understanding why an answer is possible" (Stewart, 1996).

When I came into teaching, I hoped to be able to help those in my classes reach that understanding and to be able to see mathematics for what it is, rather than to see it as it is seen by so many others. In order to do this, however, they need to learn the core skills. They need those tools to be able to reach an understanding and to be able to explore the subject. Learning the rules and the algorithms is, for the mathematician, the equivalent of the musician learning their scales or an artist learning the different techniques in drawing or painting. These are important things to know in order to create, but they are not what the subject is.

In teaching, there is often a heavy focus on learning these skills and algorithms. They are there in the national curriculum and they are there on the exam specification. In a world where exam results are key, they are of the utmost importance. We need to teach them, but we do our subject and our learners a disservice if we teach *only* them.

When I came into teaching, the maths GCSE exams were set in a way that these skills were usually tested in a formulaic manner. Students were often taught to look for key words in a question to allow them to know which algorithm to follow in order to arrive successfully at the right answer. This led to a system that meant each year I would receive students into my A Level classes who had achieved great grades at GCSE but had no real understanding of what maths was, or in some cases why the things they were doing worked. They would invariably struggle when it came to A Level, with its greater emphasis on the creative side, questions set so they could be answered using different branches of maths, branches merged together in questions and understanding much more essential.

Then the reforms came, the GCSE saw things added to it, but the biggest change was to the style of exam. Now the questions are less formulaic, less predictable and require more understanding and creativity to solve them. This often means that just teaching the maths is not going to be enough. This allows our students to become more A Level ready and also helps keep the attention of some of them who would become bored by the formulaic method.

The idea that teaching the maths alone was not enough is something that has always resonated with me. I noticed early that students would often get lost when it came to contextualised questions in exam conditions. I had been told while training to include contextualised questions as standard in my teaching to offset this; however, it didn't seem to work all that well. I suggest that this is due to its being much easier to spot that you need to use Pythagoras' Theorem to solve a question when your learning objective at the start that states the goal is "to solve questions in context using Pythagoras' theorem", or even just because that's the thing you learned today.

From this idea, I started to consider how I approach maths problems. I do a lot of maths recreationally, I enjoy it and it keeps my skills sharp. I began to consider the skills I was using in order to do this. It comes down to a couple of things. Firstly, I have a deep skill set when it comes to maths and can draw upon knowledge from a variety of branches of mathematics to seek solutions. This part is covered by ensuring the curriculum is taught. Secondly, and perhaps more importantly, I have ideas as to where to look for starting points. I think that this is a key skill, and that we need to be able to impart this and other problem-solving skills to our students.

Understanding and problem solving became something of a focus for me in my early teaching career, and was actually the subject of my MA dissertation. There was a variety of writing available on the subject and I found some of it very interesting. There is an excellent article by Skemp (1976) which discusses understanding. He refers to algorithmic proficiency as "instrumental understanding", meaning they can do it as a process but do not understand why. He also talks about "relational understanding" which is a deeper understanding of why the concepts work. The latter enables students to be able to apply this to new problems and contexts. Pólya (1971) suggests that teachers can stifle the relational understanding of their students by only setting routine problems.

This got me thinking about problem solving. Lockhart (2009) defines a good problem, as "one you don't know how to solve". This quote is one that really resonates with me. When I do attempt a question, I get a much greater satisfaction from solving it if the solution is not immediately obvious. There is a variety of literature about problem solving which tells us that it is important for our learners' development of relational understanding that they are allowed to attempt this type of problem, (Avital and Shettleworth, 1968, Pearcy 2015, Romberg 1994, and Silver and Marshal 1990).

One of my favourite pieces of literature on problem solving is by Pólya (1971) and in it he talks of the role of the teacher, and how one of the primary things we need to do is help learners improve their understanding. He suggests that one of the best ways we can manage that is to explicitly teach problem-solving skills. He put forward a framework for problem solving which boils down to Understanding the problem, devising a plan, carrying out the plan, and checking the result. Hembree (1992) found that the teaching of these types of framework, or heuristic, does lead to an improvement in problem solving. However, Schoenfield (1992) and Foster (2013) both express concern that by teaching these frameworks we can run the risk of breaking problem solving down into an algorithmic process, and we will in essence be back to square one. One way these authors suggest we can combat this is by choosing the problems that we set very carefully.

It was through all this that I realised that achieving the goal of having learners who have a deep understanding of the concepts and an ability to apply those concepts into new contexts can come through a three-pronged approach.

1. Embed the core skills required

2. Help students build a problem-solving skill set

3. Give them problems they can't do, allow them time to get stuck and then to solve them.

Embedding the core skills should be a given, and this comes through having the right curriculum and teaching it well. However, as well as this we need to ensure we are allowing time for the other two prongs.

One way I have found success at building a problem-solving skill set with students is to share my thought processes through modelling problem solving. Sometimes this might be sharing problems I have done recently and then talking them through it, or occasionally sharing problems I have yet to solve and trying to work with classes to find the solution. By modelling this process, I can show them the four stages that Pólya (1971) mentions

- understanding the problem
- devising a plan
- carrying out the plan
- checking the result.

During the modelling process, I would talk to them about how I come to understand the problem. If I do not understand it at first, what do I know about it? Can I frame it in other terms? Do the things I know about them lead me to anything? Then I would move on to the devising a plan: Do I have enough information to get to the answer? How can I get more information? Then carrying out the plan, and finally how to check the results.

I think this fourth point is important and often overlooked by learners. They can often trust their process too much and not take the time to check properly. For some, they do not even know how to check. We need to make sure we are giving them the skills needed to check, or when we tell them to "check through your answers", it will do no good.

I view answer checking as a few things. When questions are contextualised, then we need to make some sanity checks. Does the answer seem reasonable in the context? If you are calculating an estimate for how many days in a month it might rain and you have an answer over 31 then it can't be right etc. Then we need to check for errors, this can often be hard, but it just involved looking at each line of working and making sure it follows onto the next in logical fashion. Finally, there is a third check; can you solve the problem a different way? and if so, is the answer the same? This is often the best check.

Another thing I have found to be effective in building these skills is the use of "goal-free" problems. These come in many forms, some are written to be goal free and some are exam (or other) questions with the question part removed. One example might be a right-angled triangle with expressions for sides, there are many questions that could be asked around this, but without including them it allows learners the freedom to explore what they know and what else they can find out, and this is vitally important to the early stages of problem solving.

The third prong is the problem setting. We need to allow our students time to get stuck and to wrestle with problems while building these skills. As I mentioned earlier, this cannot be done by setting a contextualised Pythagoras question at the end of a lesson, or sequence of lessons, about Pythagoras' Theorem. This tells the learners what they need to do. We need to allow time to tackle problems that are off topic. Maybe it is something that you taught fairly recently or maybe it is something you've not taught in a while. Maybe it is just something that combines together branches. These problems can be posed as starter tasks to any lesson, or if you're lucky enough to have some time available in the scheme for learning then you can dedicate lessons to it. It helps to have a bank of puzzles and questions. Sometime the exams (GCSE/A Level) throw up brilliant questions and I keep a file of them. Twitter is also a great place to come across them as well as blogs and other social media.

References

Avital, S.M. and Shettleworth, S.J. 1968. *Objectives for Mathematics Learning; Some Ideas for the Teacher.* Toronto: Ontario Institute for Studies in Education.

Foster, C. 2013. 'Mathematical etudes: Embedding opportunities for developing procedure', *International Journal of Mathematical Education in Science and Technology.* 44 (5), pp. 765–774; available online via **www.foster77.co.uk**

Hembree, R. 1992. Experiments and relational studies in problem solving: a meta-analysis. *Journal for Research in Mathematics Education* 33 (3), pp. 242–273.

Lockhart, P. 2009. *A mathematician's lament: How school cheats us out of our most fascinating and imaginative art form.* New York: Bellevue Literary Press.

Pearcy, D. 2015. 'Reflections on patient problem solving', *Mathematics Teaching* 247, pp. 39–40.

Pólya, G. 1971. *How to solve it: A new aspect of mathematical method.* 2nd ed. Princeton, NJ: Princeton University Press, 1971.

Reynolds, D. and Muijs, D. 1999. 'The effective teaching of mathematics: A review of research', *School Leadership & Management.* 19 (3), pp. 273–288.

Romberg, T.A. 1994. 'Classroom instruction that fosters mathematical thinking and problem solving: Connections between theory and practice', in: Schoenfeld, A.H. ed. *Mathematical Thinking and Problem*

Solving. Hilsdale, New Jersey: Lawrence Erlbaum Associates, pp. 287–304

Schoenfeld, A.H. 1992. 'Learning to think mathematically: Problem solving, metacognition and sense making in mathematics', in: Grouws, D.A. ed. *Handbook of Research on Mathematics Teaching and Learning*. New York: Maxwell Macmillan International, pp. 334–370.

Silver, E.A. and Marshall, S.P. 1990. 'Mathematical and scientific problem solving: Findings, issues and instructional implications', in: Jones, B.F. and Idol, L. eds. *Dimensions of Thinking and Cognitive Instruction*. Hilsdale, New Jersey, United States: Lawrence Erlbaum Associates, pp. 265–290.

Skemp, R.R. 1976. Relational understanding and instrumental understanding. *Mathematics Teaching*. 77, pp. 20–27.

Stewart, I. 1996. *From Here to Infinity*. New York: Oxford University Press.

17   *Choose Your Questions Carefully*

Ed Southall

There is so much nuance in teaching mathematics effectively. Take for example, the art of designing a good question. This seemingly simple task is surprisingly complicated to do well, and incredibly easy to do badly. Understandably, priorities for lesson planning and task design often focus on topic coverage, behaviour, having a set of slides that help your exposition, and having a set of questions that enable practice of a skill; but whilst we might rely on a good textbook or online resource to provide solid questioning structure, the reality is that many resources do not carefully consider *how* their questions are designed. There are many facets to this area of maths teaching, and to assume expertise in all of them is perhaps unwise. Take as example, the importance of sequencing – the careful selection of *what comes next. A* common mistake in teaching is to not carefully plan for the transition between what examples the teacher is demonstrating, and the first questions students attempt independently. In terms of the common practice of 'I do' (teacher-led examples), 'we do' (class-led examples) and 'you do' (independent work), we are referring here to the transition between 'we do' and 'you do'. As a case study, let's look at solving linear equations. Consider the three examples below:

$$3x + 5 = 20,$$
$$9 + 3x = 15,$$
$$5x + 2 = 30.$$

Now, let's assume that $3x + 5 = 20$ is part of the teacher demonstration. It's a fairly simple example, with two steps required to solve it. A likely approach would be to subtract five from both sides, then divide both sides by 3 to arrive at the answer:

$$3x + 5 = 20$$
$$3x = 15$$
$$x = 5.$$

An important thing to notice here is that it took only two steps. This is likely to be the focus of the lesson (the lesson objective could be something like 'solve two-step linear equations'), and our analysis could, and often does, end there. However, beyond that, we should also take note of the smaller but equally important details here:

- The equation is of the form $ax + b = c$

- a, b and c are all positive

- This equation requires *subtraction,* followed by *division* to solve

- a and b are single digit numbers

- c is a low multiple of 10

- The answer is a positive integer – or more accurately, $(c - b)$ is a multiple of a

This may feel like over-analysis, but each of these factors is important to help us develop a sense of the perceived difficulty of the question. This in turn informs how to construct the next question, and acts as a predictor for how well students will cope with it – how intuitive the approach is compared to the previous example.

Now consider the first and second question together:

$$3x + 5 = 20,$$
$$9 + 3x = 15.$$

Let's assume these are part of the 'we do' phase of teaching, so the teacher is still addressing the whole class when discussing how they are solved. This means that any difficulties or questions that arise can be addressed by the teacher (or posed to students) and the whole class learns from it. The signal here is that we can change elements of the question without risking a large proportion of the class losing their way and seeking further guidance in a way that is unmanageable for the teacher. (Imagine for example, ten hands going up during independent work and having to handle each query individually.)

So, what has changed? Let's compare them side by side:

$$3x + 5 = 20 \qquad\qquad 9 + 3x = 15$$
$$3x = 15 \qquad\qquad 3x = 6$$
$$x = 5 \qquad\qquad x = 2$$

What is the same, and what is different about these two examples?

$3x + 5 = 20$	$9 + 3x = 15$	Same?
The equation is of the form $ax + b = c$	The equation is of the form $b + ax = c$	**No**
a, b and c are all positive	a, b and c are all positive	Yes
This equation requires *subtraction*, followed by *division* to solve	This equation requires *subtraction*, followed by *division* to solve	Yes
a and b are single digit numbers	a and b are single digit numbers	Yes
c is a contextually simple number	c is a contextually simple number	Yes
$(c - b)$ is a multiple of a	$(c - b)$ is a multiple of a	Yes
$a = 3$	$a = 3$	Yes
$b = 5$	$b = 9$	**No**
$c = 20$	$c = 15$	**No**

A principle of good sequencing is that very little should change between examples, and what *does* change is the thing you want to focus on explicitly. This is a key component of what is often referred to as **variation theory**. Whilst we are being forensic in our analysis here, at this level of detail you can see that we have changed **four** components of our question. That means four new things to think about, and potentially four things to draw attention to in our teacher exposition. Changing multiple things can also mask what the general effect of changing **one** component has on the structure of the equation and the way to solve it. Incidentally, perhaps the most significant change between the two equations is moving from the form $ax + b = c$ to $b + ax = c$. You may be wondering why considering the value of it in terms of its being a "contextually simple" number is important. This is simply related to cognitive load and our ability to handle numbers for mental arithmetic. If numbers are more awkward, they will take more time, effort and focus to work with, which is time taken away from what we *want* students to focus on. This adds to a general feeling of perceived difficulty around a question. For example, it's easier to spot both that 15 is a multiple of 5, and that there are three 5's in 15, than it is to spot, say, 102 is a multiple of 6 and that there are seventeen 6's in 102.

It's important to note here that this isn't about what is the *wrong* approach, and what is the *right* approach. Instead, it is better to think in terms of what component you want to teach, and how efficiently you can do it. For example, if I want to teach about the similarities and differences between the forms $ax + b = c$ and $b + ax = c$, and subsequently the effect that has (or doesn't have) on solving equations, then it would be an efficient approach to focus on that change, and only that change. Hence my two examples could be:

$$3x + 5 = 20,$$
$$5 + 3x = 20.$$

Of course, this is not going to take up an entire lesson, but it is an important sub-skill required to be able to tackle all forms of solving a two-step linear equation and should at least be a consideration when planning.

Conversely, if I want to focus on, say, making the decision as to whether I need to add or subtract to solve an equation, my examples could be:

$$3x + 5 = 20,$$
$$3x - 5 = 20.$$

But wait a second... We've fallen straight into the problem highlighted before. More than one thing has changed, even though it looks like it's only the operator. Inadvertently, $(20 - 5)$ is a multiple of 3, but $(20 + 5)$ is **not** a multiple of 3. This is going to cause a headache for students and distract from the focus: deciding what operator to use. There are two potential workarounds: the first is to make sure that our teacher instruction is simply to identify the next step to solve the equation, rather than solving the equation in full. The second option is to choose more sensibly for a, b *and* c:

$$10x + 5 = 25,$$
$$10x - 5 = 25.$$

Now we have ensured that the only change is the thing we want to focus on, which keeps us focused on it, and the effect it has. Again, the point to all this is to think carefully about *what* we want students to learn, and the most efficient way to get them there.

You can see from these examples that lesson objectives alone are often too broad to help us think about specific questions. If we approached the design of each question in this topic with 'are they solving a two-step linear equation here?', that isn't specific enough to help us navigate the journey students need to make to be competent in this area, and it risks a rockier route, fraught with hidden misconceptions. In turn, it makes a teacher's role harder as we attempt to diagnose what piece of the puzzle is missing. If this is starting to feel complicated, well, it *is* complicated! It also helps shine a light on what is, and what is not, a good resource, whether it was written by you or not. Let's look at the three examples now that we appreciate the nuance of task design a little more:

$$3x + 5 = 20,$$
$$9 + 3x = 15,$$
$$5x + 2 = 30.$$

Remember that our original intent was to use $5x + 2 = 30$ as the first question in an independent task, without any whole-class teacher input. Remember too, that for independent work, we as teachers need to feel confident that they can do those questions, for the most part, on their own. If they can't, then our role risks becoming one of slowly working around the room, student by student, trying to unpick where their understanding isn't aligned with our own, hoping that the last doesn't misbehave or sit doing nothing until we get there. Let's do one more comparison table, this time between $9 + 3x = 15$ and $5x + 2 = 30$:

$9 + 3x = 15$	$5x + 2 = 30$	Same?
The equation is of the form $ax + b = c$	The equation is of the form $b + ax = c$	**No**
a, b and c are all positive	a, b and c are all positive	Yes
This equation requires *subtraction,* followed by *division* to solve	This equation requires *subtraction,* followed by *division* to solve	Yes
a and b are single digit numbers	a and b are single digit numbers	Yes
c is a contextually simple number	c is a contextually simple number	Yes
$(c - b)$ is a multiple of a	$(c - b)$ is **not** a multiple of a	**No**
$a = 3$	$a = 5$	**No**
$b = 9$	$b = 2$	**No**
$c = 15$	$c = 30$	**No**

Whilst we can debate whether 30 is a contextually simple number for the equation $5x + 2 = 30$, it is clear here that there are quite a lot of differences between the two examples. The most significant difference is that $(c - b)$ is **not** a multiple of a in $5x + 2 = 30$. This means the answer will not be a positive integer. Does that matter in reality? For teachers, probably not – we are experts, and we are adept at handling a variety of things at once when it comes to maths. Decimal, fraction, or remainder, we can handle it and shrug it off. For students however, we have just burdened them with a whole new set of problems to deal with. Primarily, we have undone any expectation of predictability in a new area of learning. The examples we used behaved in one way, and now, on their own, students are finding their examples are behaving in another way. It's not what they expected, and now their confidence is at risk of depleting. Whilst, as part of our lesson design, we may wish to test the boundaries of their knowledge within a topic, doing so within the first question of an independent task will typically not end well, and will result in several unconfident hands being raised followed by an improvised round of re-teaching.

In summary, let them tread the well-trodden path – make their work feel predictable, at least at first, to help build confidence and help them focus on what matters – feeling successful, identifying behaviours within the maths, and understanding them. We've barely scratched the surface of good task design, but already you can see that it's a very complex and thought-provoking area of teaching maths.

18 Numbers Count in Examples and Questions

Paul Rowlandson

Does it matter what numbers we choose when writing questions? Surely the numbers are just arbitrary and what matters is the method! Well, sometimes the choice of numbers in a question or example can obscure the method. This chapter explores a variety of situations where it is worth taking caution over what numbers are used.

When introducing a new mathematical idea to a class, the first example they see can be the initial step on the path to understanding. The numbers that are used in these introductory examples can affect how the idea is perceived by students. Unfortunately, some numbers create ambiguity that can tempt students towards misconception. This is particularly the case when it is easy to make incorrect deductions from correct calculations. Or in other words: when you can do the 'right thing' for the wrong reasons.

Let's say students are being introduced to the concept of 'squaring' for the first time. What might students think if this was the first example they saw?

$$2^2 = 2 \times 2 = 4.$$

They can see that they are multiplying 2 by 2, but what is the meaning of each 2? On one hand, a student might think that the "big two" is being multiplied by itself and the "little two" shows how many parts there are to the multiplication. That is what we hope they would see! Then, they would calculate three squared by multiplying 3 by 3.

$$2^2 = 2 \times 2 = 4,$$
$$3^2 = 3 \times 3 = 9.$$

However, that is not the only interpretation available for why we are multiplying 2 by 2. A student could assume that they are simply "multiplying the big number and little number together". This would mean that when they try and square other numbers, they will be tempted to do the same again.

$$2^2 = 2 \times 2 = 4,$$
$$3^2 = 3 \times 2 = 6.$$

The fact that both the index and the base contain the same number makes the reasoning behind the calculation slightly ambiguous. To someone seeing this calculation for the first time, the correct reasoning is quite subtle and the wrong reasoning ("we multiplied the big two by the little two") probably seems like the more obvious explanation. Therefore, using the number two for squaring is probably best avoided until students have understood the true meaning of the index.

Pesky 'number two' can cause similar problems with other aspects of indices too. Take the following examples of index laws:

$a^2 \times a^2 = a^4$ *"Has the 4 in the answer come from doing 2 + 2 or 2 × 2?"*

$(a^2)^2 = a^4$ *"Has the 4 in the answer come from doing 2 + 2 or 2 × 2?"*

$a^4 \div a^2 = a^2$ *"Has the 2 in the answer come from doing 4 − 2 or 4 ÷ 2?"*

$4^{\frac{1}{2}} = 2$ *"Has the 2 in the answer come from doing $\frac{1}{2}$ of 4 or $\sqrt{4}$?"*

The problem in each of these cases is that it is possible to obtain the correct answer from an incorrect calculation. In situations where a student solves one of these questions, it can be difficult for a teacher to tell from their answer if they have understood it properly. Even worse, it could lead to a misconception being validated for a student by being told they are correct.

Problems like these don't just lie with the number two. Let's look at some other ways that numbers can lay conceptual traps in other topics. For example, percentage of amounts:

$$10\% \ of \ 80 = 80 \div 10 = 8$$

A teacher would want students to understand that the reason we divide by 10 in this case is because there are ten lots of 10% in 100%.

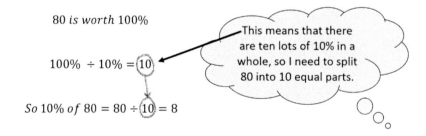

80 *is worth* 100%

100% ÷ 10% = ⑩

So 10% *of* 80 = 80 ÷ ⑩ = 8

This means that there are ten lots of 10% in a whole, so I need to split 80 into 10 equal parts.

But this reasoning is once again fairly subtle, especially compared to the more appealing (incorrect) explanation: the 10 in the division corresponds with the 10 in the percentage.

$$10\% \; of \; 80 = 80 \div 10 = 8$$

A student could answer a whole exercise of "find 10%" problems correctly while completely misunderstanding what they are doing. Furthermore, if a student gets too comfortable with the notion that "you find 10% by dividing by 10" then they may then extend this to think, "You find 5% dividing by 5." However, it is worth noting that students quite often learn to find other percentages of amounts first before they look at finding 10%, so this might not be an issue. Nonetheless, it is always worth being mindful of the potential pitfall that a student may fall into with their reasoning.

There are also cases in data handling where numbers can make false assumptions more attractive than correct reasoning. When students are learning to calculate frequency density for histograms, we would want students to see clearly from a worked example that the frequency is being divided by the class width for its group. However, in each of the examples below, the first row provides an alternative way to interpret the meaning of the divisor.

Weight, w (grams)	Frequency	Frequency Density
$0 \leq w < 10$	25	$25 \div 10 = 2.5$
.	.	.
.	.	.
.	.	.

"You use the upper bound of the group (like in cumulative frequency diagrams)."

Weight, w (grams)	Frequency	Frequency Density
$5 \leq w < 15$	25	$25 \div 10 = 2.5$
.	.	.
.	.	.
.	.	.

"You use the midpoint of the group (like when estimating the mean)."

Weight, w (grams)	Frequency	Frequency Density
$10 \leq w < 20$	25	$25 \div 10 = 2.5$
.	.	.
.	.	.
.	.	.

"You use the lower bound of the group."

While the frequency *is* being divided by the class-width in all cases, each one shows a potential misinterpretation for that division. Some of these wrong explanations may seem more obvious than dividing by the class width either because the divisor is visible in the row or because they have used midpoints before when dealing with data. In the example below however, there is only one explanation for where that divisor of 10 comes from: the difference between 40 and 30.

Weight, w (grams)	Frequency	Frequency Density
$30 \leq w < 40$	25	$25 \div 10 = 2.5$
.	.	.
.	.	.
.	.	.

Elsewhere in data, it can be a common misconception for students to think that the 'range' is a type of average. If it were, then you would expect the mean, median, mode and range to all be similar numbers to each other in a set of data, because they are all types of averages. This misconception can be exacerbated when students see an example like the one below.

Find the mean, median, mode and range for the set of numbers below.

$$3, 4, 6, 6, 8, 9$$

$$Mean = 6$$
$$Mode = 6$$
$$Median = 6$$
$$Range = 6$$

The example above is an extreme case because all four measures give the exact same value. But even a problem like the one below can cause similar issues:

Find the mean, median, mode and range for the set of numbers below.

$$3, 5, 5, 6, 7, 9$$

$$Mean = 5.8$$
$$Mode = 5$$
$$Median = 5.5$$
$$Range = 6$$

Students rightly get used to the idea that finding different averages for the same set of numbers often gives similar results. So, if they also see lots of examples where the range also gives a similar result to the mean, median or mode then it can be easy for them to assume that range is just another type of average. One way to steer students away from this potential misconception is to use numbers where the range is distinctly different to any of the averages. A simple way to fix this for the last example could be to increase all the numbers by 20.

Find the mean, median, mode and range for the set of numbers below.

$$23, 25, 25, 26, 27, 29$$

$$Mean = 25.8$$
$$Mode = 25$$
$$Median = 25.5$$
$$Range = 6$$

Finally, let's look at some potential number traps in geometry...

In the example below, it may not be entirely clear to a student why we have done 4 multiplied by 4 to get 16. Is it because we have multiplied the length by width? Or is it because we added all the sides together to get 4 lots of 4?

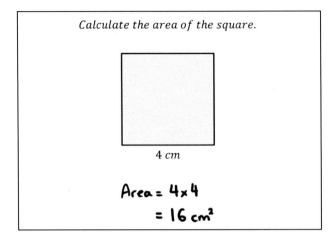

The problem in this case, like with 2 squared, is that it is possible to apply incorrect reasoning to the correct calculation. One way to distinguish between the calculations for area and perimeter is to include the units in the calculations. However, it is probably safer to avoid squares with length 4 cm altogether – or at least to begin with.

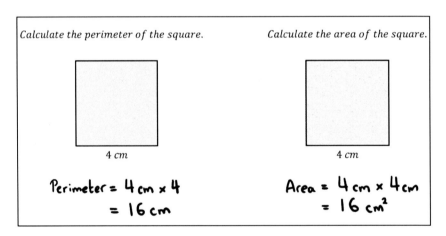

A similar point can be made about circles. One common mistake that students make is to mix up the formulae for area and circumference. Therefore, if a student calculated 12.6 cm² for the question below, could the teacher be sure that they had chosen the correct formula?

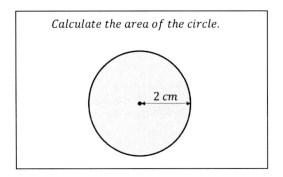

Calculate the area of the circle.

2 cm

Finally, has the student below correctly understood how to find the surface area of a cube?

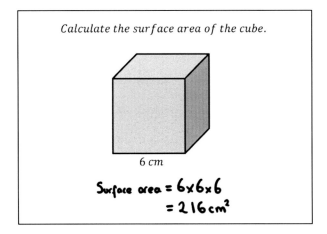

Calculate the surface area of the cube.

6 cm

Surface area = 6×6×6

= 216 cm²

The examples in this chapter have shown how some number choices can provide unwanted ambiguity around the meaning of calculations or solutions. Such ambiguity can tempt students towards incorrect deductions or make it difficult for a teacher to assess if a student has understood something correctly. If one of these are used as the first worked example students see on the board then it could send students down the wrong path, meaning that the next worked example has to work twice as hard to bring them back and down the correct path. Rather than affirming what students learned from the first worked example, it has a double job of undoing a misconception and providing clarity around more accurate reasoning. That is not to say that these questions are not interesting to explore; just that the timing of them is an important consideration.

It should be noted that while questions with 'number traps' can cause problems, they rarely appear in isolation. They are usually accompanied by explanations from the teacher or form part of a series of questions. Students also usually come to lessons equipped with some relevant prior knowledge that can help them along the way. So, if a question or example does accidently contain a 'number trap' then do not worry; there are plenty of other supportive mechanisms to keep students on the right track. Considerations about number choices simply provide an extra level of risk management during the crucial initial stages of developing understanding.

19   *Give Me an Example*

Sam Blatherwick

When I first had to teach proof I was led too often by what would gain marks in examinations. Many times I would see an answer to a given problem and find that a student had 'merely' put an example of it happening, rather than construct the algebraic proof that I was expecting. "THIS IS NOT A PROOF" I would scrawl, grumpily, across their work in green ink, as if stating this would cause the scales to fall from their eyes.

However, proof is more nuanced, more mathematical, more delicate, and, when approached in the right way, so much more joyful if you take your time to savour it. As a topic it struggles against being thrown down the path of procedure. Perhaps, those students whose work I carelessly dismissed had more of a clue than I was giving them credit for. What if what these students are doing is *feeling* the maths in a domain they have a grasp of, and maybe our job is to encourage this, and to guide them from these examples, from something plausible to something demonstrative. And far from looking down on these examples as something to be dismissed, maybe they hold the key to being able to unlock the secrets of proof.

To demonstrate how this technique can be used, let me give you an example and have a go at it before you read on:

Prove that the sum of *n* consecutive odd numbers is a multiple of *n*.

You and I, with our knowledge of summations of arithmetic series, can put together a simple algebraic proof for this. Marching through such a proof does the job, but feels somewhat blunt, ugly and without a feel for the result that we have achieved. Sure, we can liven it up with a little algebraic flair, but we can also circumvent it for a joyless slog. No, in fact, when we play with the numbers, when we encourage students to enter into a domain that they feel comfortable in, we actually find so much more with which to play.

A technique I learnt from a John Mason book was "specialising", that is to look at giving ourselves some examples to ponder. Consider

$$7 + 9 + 11 + 13 + 15 = 55.$$

We can see here that we have our sum of five consecutive odd numbers, and that our result is indeed a multiple of 5. For us to feel this however, we really want to emphasise it, so we show how it is divisible by 5:

$$7 + 9 + 11 + 13 + 15 = 55 = 5 \times 11.$$

This gives us another number to ponder and to establish patterns with. We can continue by writing some more patterns down and start to look at the numbers we get.

$$9 + 11 + 13 + 15 + 17 = 65 = 5 \times 13,$$

$$25 + 27 + 29 + 31 + 33 = 145 = 5 \times 29.$$

So far we have demonstrated the result for n being 5, so we change the value of n to get more results, let's try 6:

$$3 + 5 + 7 + 9 + 11 + 13 = 48 = 6 \times 8,$$

$$11 + 13 + 15 + 17 + 19 + 21 = 96 = 6 \times 16.$$

Now we have lots of tasty examples to sink our teeth into. Firstly, and importantly, we spot that it works. We have not found a counter example. We have shown that all the examples so far are true and this adds to plausibility to our sense that the result is true. It heightens our trust in the statement of the proof. The neat proof using sums of arithmetic series earlier wasn't doing that for a student not yet au fait with all of the algebraic techniques that may be used by a maths teacher. It makes it look like witchcraft by the gatekeepers.

Next, with all that data in front of us we can start to make judgements about what is going on here. We can spot that the middle is important and this gives us a crucial inroad to generalisation. The middle was easier to spot with 5, so let us work with this example:

$$7 + 9 + 11 + 13 + 15 = 55 = 5 \times 11.$$

We knew the middle number was crucial, and so we replace the middle number with m, and think about the relationships that this number has with the other numbers around it. Algebra is introduced in reference to our example, built upon the foundations of the example:

$$(m - 4) + (m - 2) + m + (m + 2) + (m + 4) = 5 \times m.$$

Through replacing the middle number with m we have demonstrated the result for $n = 5$.

Now we move onto the case of six consecutive odd numbers.

$$5 + 7 + 9 + 11 + 13 + 15 = 60 = 6 \times 10.$$

Here the "middle" number is 10, but it doesn't exist in our sum. We still, however, make $m = 10$. So $9 = (m - 1)$ and $11 = (m + 1)$.

This gives us the sum:

$$(m - 5) + (m - 3) + (m - 1) + (m + 1) + (m + 3) + (m + 5) = 6 \times m$$

and this demonstrates our result for $n = 6$.

Now we can further generalise by looking at what we have just done. We have shown it for 5 and 6, but what relation do the sums that we have written have to 5 and 6?
5 started with $(m - 4)$ and ended with $(m + 4)$.
6 started with $(m - 5)$ and ended with $(m + 5)$.
We can assert that n will start with $(m - n + 1)$ and end with $(m + n - 1)$.

$$(m - n + 1) + (m - n + 3) + \cdots + (m + n - 3) + (m + n - 1) = m \times n.$$

Hence we build a proof of the result from the examples that led to the result.

However, when we did examples, maybe there was something completely different to spot? Maybe there was another pattern hiding in there? Maybe your examples went like this:

$$1 + 3 + 5 + 7 + 9 + 11 + 13 + 15 = 64 = 8 \times 8,$$
$$3 + 5 + 7 + 9 + 11 + 13 + 15 + 17 = 80 = 8 \times 10,$$
$$5 + 7 + 9 + 11 + 13 + 15 + 17 + 19 = 96 = 8 \times 12.$$

There is great worth in working systematically, with a basic start and a consistent layout, for noticing underlying patterns.

Why do we know it will be a multiple of 8 each time? We know this because:

$$5 + 7 + 9 + 11 + 13 + 15 + 17 + 19 = 96 = 8 \times 12$$
$$\downarrow \quad \downarrow \quad \downarrow \quad \downarrow \quad \downarrow \quad \downarrow \quad \downarrow \quad \downarrow \qquad\qquad \downarrow$$
$$7 + 9 + 11 + 13 + 15 + 17 + 19 + 21 = 112 = 8 \times 14$$

What do we notice about the connection between the numbers? We add on two each time. We add on two 8 times, and hence, we will end up with a multiple of 8 again.

And for each different value of n we know that this will be true. Take a pair of examples from 5 earlier:

$$7 + 9 + 11 + 13 + 15 = 55,$$
$$9 + 11 + 13 + 15 + 17 = 65.$$

We can observe that this is true in this case.

This proceeds almost inductively, in that if we can prove the first result is true each time, then we can show that they are all true. Of course, the first result in each of the sequences has its own moment of wonder:

$$1 = 1$$
$$1 + 3 = 4$$
$$1 + 3 + 5 = 9$$
$$1 + 3 + 5 + 7 = 16$$
$$1 + 3 + 5 + 7 + 9 = 25.$$

Look back, and think about the middle numbers in these sums.

$$1 + \cdots + (2n - 1) = n^2.$$

So $(2p + 1) + \cdots + (2p + 2n - 1) = n^2 + 2pn = n(n + 2p)$.

Hence the sums are always a multiple of n.

Here we can demonstrate how a result that we obtain can show us a new beautiful path of noticing by specialising again. We can look back at our previous results and look at what they can tell us about the numbers.

$$3 + 5 + 7 + 9 + 11 + 13 = 48 = 36 + 12 = 6^2 + 2 \times 6,$$

$$7 + 9 + 11 + 13 + 15 + 17 + 19 + 21 = 112 = 64 + 48 = 8^2 + 6 \times 8.$$

Through looking at how the numbers play with each other we can craft other results of beauty. Note the sequence:

$$2 = 2$$
$$8 = 3 + 5$$
$$18 = 4 + 6 + 8$$
$$32 = 5 + 7 + 9 + 11$$
$$50 = 6 + 8 + 10 + 12 + 14.$$

Another "inductive pattern" could be spotted as follows, taking $n = 7$

$$5 + \boxed{7 + 9 + 11 + 13 + 15 + 17} = 77 = 7 \times 11$$

$$\boxed{7 + 9 + 11 + 13 + 15 + 17} + 19 = 77 - 5 + 19 = 91$$

$$7 + \boxed{9 + 11 + 13 + 15 + 17 + 19} = 77 - 5 + 19 = 91$$

$$\boxed{9 + 11 + 13 + 15 + 17 + 19} + 21 = 91 - 7 + 21 = 105$$

In general, we always take the previous result, lose the first number and always add on something $2n$ bigger. In all of these cases, the pattern is easier to see when we observe it in the world of numbers and their interactions with each other, than it is to see it when tackling it with algebra initially.

When late GCSE or early A-level students join us, they are often comfortable to play in the world of number, but less confident with algebra, and in particular, algebra representing mathematical objects. The process of specialising to generalise can be powerful, playful and joyful.

Try these similar proofs for size, giving examples and generalising from the examples, rather than building from your existing knowledge.

1. Prove that the sum of two consecutive powers of two is always divisible by 3.

2. Prove that $4^x - 2^x + 1 \geq \frac{3}{4}$ for all real values of x.

3. Two points A and B have coordinates (u, v) and (v, u) respectively.
    They lie on the curve $y = x^2 + bx + c$.
    Prove that the intercept of the curve is $u + v + uv$.

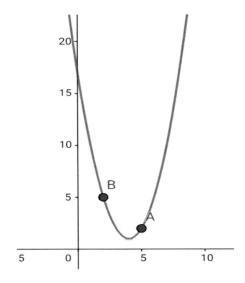

20   *More Depth, Less Speed*

Jo Morgan

'Rapid teaching'

Have you ever worked with a maths teacher who proudly progresses through the curriculum quicker than other teachers, no matter what class they are teaching? They race through topic after topic, skipping the fundamentals and focusing on acceleration. It's a pedagogical style which seems old-fashioned, but it's still surprisingly prevalent in schools. I call this style of pedagogy 'rapid teaching'. It's pretty much the opposite of 'teaching for mastery', however you interpret that idea.

Proponents of rapid teaching think that if their students learn a procedure quickly, then their teaching must have been highly effective. They think that if students can respond to questions correctly in a lesson, this is evidence of understanding. They confuse speed of teaching with quality of teaching.

These teachers think that the only way to challenge and engage students is to accelerate them onto more advanced topics.

> *I skipped rounding with Year 7, they've done it before anyway and it would have bored them. We've moved onto calculating with bounds and they totally get it. I had them all doing GCSE questions within the hour.*

Rushing through topics at breakneck speed gives no opportunity for reasoning and no opportunity to develop any depth of knowledge whatsoever. If memory is the residue of thought, what a shame that many students don't seem to get the chance to think.

Students experiencing this style of teaching will only ever have superficial understanding of the topics they've been taught. Their understanding of mathematics will be 'a mile wide and an inch deep'.

Advocates of rapid teaching have a short-term view. They teach each concept in one or two lessons, and jump quickly from topic to topic. They end up with plenty of time for revision before assessments, and their students become well-practised at recalling the facts and procedures they have recently been shown. These students then get good test grades, and the teachers claim, "My way works well". Unfortunately, these students are likely to encounter great difficulty at A level, where deep understanding of fundamental mathematical concepts is absolutely essential. But that is of little concern to the teachers who opt for rapid teaching. Short-term success is everything to them. This is often motivated by counterproductive annual performance targets based on results, as well as lesson observation cultures which seek evidence of 'progress'.

In a recent survey, **39% of respondents agreed with the statement**

> *I challenge students by teaching them more advanced topics.*

This is a concern. Acceleration is rarely the best way to provide challenge. Perhaps these teachers are accelerating their students because they simply don't know how to challenge without acceleration. So they move on, because they just don't know where else to go.

The teachers who rush, but against their better judgment

There are many teachers who have convinced themselves that rushing is 'a good thing'. But there are just as many teachers who are forced to rush against their will.

Picture the scene: it's the start of the summer term and end of year assessments are looming. You look at your scheme of work for Year 7 and see that in the next six weeks you need to teach angles, equations, area, ratio, averages and pie charts.

> *I can't teach all of those topics in such a short period of time. I'll have to skip something.*
>
> *You can't do that, it's not fair on the students if they get assessed on topics they haven't been taught.*
>
> *But there's not enough time to properly teach all of those topics.*
>
> *You'll just have to make it fit. Move quickly. They've done a lot of it at primary school anyway.*

The argument which suggests 'they've done it before so skip it' is very common. It is highly flawed for two key reasons:

- regardless of what students have studied before, there is *always* an opportunity to teach a topic in greater depth. It's only a lack of expertise on the teacher's part that stands in the way.

- in the 2019 Year 6 SATs 79% of pupils achieved the 'expected standard' in mathematics – and it's important to note that **to achieve expected standard they only had to score 53%** on their maths exams at the end of Year 6. Just like at GCSE, they are able 'pass' with huge gaps in their knowledge and understanding.

Making a sweeping assumption that secondary school students are secure in every topic on the primary curriculum is simply not sensible. That would be like an A Level teacher assuming that all students are totally fluent in all aspects of algebraic manipulation, and ploughing ahead with calculus from Day One.

There's no need for us to make assumptions about prior knowledge when we can easily make informed decisions about the appropriate starting points in our teaching. If we are going to 'skip' parts of the Key Stage 3 curriculum based on the claim that our students 'have done it before', we must check prior knowledge and understanding carefully.

In secondary schools, it's important that the Year 7 scheme of work features exciting new maths, but it should also revisit and strengthen understanding in previously taught topics. Remember, it is possible (and in fact eminently sensible) to teach topics like angles, rounding, fractions, percentages, area and proportion in Year 7 but at *a greater level of depth* than taught previously. It's entirely possible to do this in an utterly engaging and challenging manner, if there's adequate time to do so. Many teachers acknowledge this but feel that they simply aren't given the opportunity. Schemes of work which fail to allow ample time to fully explore each topic put teachers in positions of ongoing conflict.

A recent survey showed that **over 40% of teachers often feel rushed in their teaching**. And **64% of teachers agree with the statement "I feel like I sometimes teach topics too quickly"**.

The solution normally lies in curriculum design. If your scheme of work has been created by a proponent of rapid teaching, you're never going to have the opportunity to do anything other than skim the surface of each topic.

What depth looks like

Let's imagine we have a teacher who:
  a. understands the long-term benefits of teaching for depth of knowledge

b. works in a school where they are given ample time for effective
    teaching

This situation is ideal. So the question then becomes, *what could this
teaching look like?*

This essentially comes down to two key considerations for each topic on
the curriculum: sequencing and lesson content. How should we progress
through the topic? And what examples, explanations and activities
should feature in our lessons? How can we challenge and engage our
students?

Challenge and engagement comes from exploring misconceptions,
methods and representations. It comes from getting our students
thinking backwards, generating their own examples and developing
connections between topics. It comes from reasoning, solving problems
and doing puzzles. There are a great many rich mathematical
experiences that our students would benefit from ... but of course, like
everything, it's all about balance. We definitely want to avoid flitting
between disconnected topics, teaching superficial procedural
knowledge and focusing on short-term performance. But at the same
time we must avoid the opposite: dragging topics out by showing
students every possible example, planning lessons featuring multiple
activities but no cohesion, and failing to engage students through
effective use of pace, variety and challenge.

This isn't about spoon-feeding, and it's not about 'going slowly'. This is
about seeking out opportunities for challenge and deep thinking *within*
topics, and not missing out on rich and meaningful learning
opportunities by moving on too quickly.

A Case Study: Pythagoras' Theorem

In a recent survey of nearly 800 secondary maths teachers, the majority
work in schools where Pythagoras' Theorem is first introduced in Year
9. This surprises me. Pythagoras' Theorem is absolutely perfect for Year
8 in my opinion. The prerequisite knowledge is squares and roots,
calculator use and rounding, all of which is typically taught in Year 7.
Pythagoras' Theorem fits well in Year 8 because it can then be revisited
in Year 9 when students are doing trigonometry, another key feature of
the Key Stage 3 curriculum. By introducing Pythagoras' Theorem and
trigonometry in the same year, this feels like a missed opportunity.

This wasn't the only thing that surprised me when teachers were surveyed about their Key Stage 3 schemes of work. Where suggested time allocations are given for each topic, **42% of respondents said that they get four hours or less to teach Pythagoras.** This seems like an incredibly short amount of time for such a fundamental topic. 48% of teachers said they have between four and eight hours, which I still think is rather rushed. Only 10% of teachers have more than two weeks to explore this beautiful topic with their students.

What could 'in depth' teaching of Pythagoras look like?

We'd certainly want to start by spending some time reviewing and mastering the prerequisites. So perhaps we might have a lesson or two exploring roots and squares, both with and without a calculator, and another lesson recapping rounding. We shouldn't be teaching Pythagoras until students have a good understanding of squares, roots and rounding, and it's a good opportunity to recap and deepen understanding of both.

Next we have the introduction of Pythagoras' Theorem itself. There's work to be done on labelling sides, on finding the length of the hypotenuse and finding the length of a leg. Whilst many teachers do all of this in one lesson, I need at last three lessons to do it justice. There's some history of Pythagoras in there too, and depending on the class perhaps a look at some proofs. Of course, the amount of time we spend on each part of the sequence depends on the class in front of us – it's vital to respond to our ongoing assessment of students' understanding, and adapt our plans accordingly.

Once our students are able to work fluently with Pythagoras Theorem to find missing lengths, we can have a go at some problem solving. This will include worded problems (where students need to draw a sketch) and multi-step problems (stacked triangles and the like). The use of exact values mid-calculation comes into play at this point – this is a key learning point in the development of a mathematician so worth spending time on.

At this point I'd do a whole lesson on the converse of Pythagoras' Theorem, and another exploring Pythagorean triples. A lesson on finding the distance between two points on a graph using Pythagoras' Theorem is worthwhile too. Depending on the class, we could also spend some time on surds, including giving exact answers as simplified surds. There are some lovely pattern-spotting investigations we could do at this point.

And then of course we have 3D Pythagoras. Beyond basic cuboids, problems involving Pythagoras' Theorem in three dimensions can get rather complex, so this needs some time.

To conclude our teaching of Pythagoras' Theorem we'd have some consolidation, mixed practice and assessment. We'd certainly want to take a look at some problems where Pythagoras is incorporated into other topics (such as those involving area, perimeter, similarity and ratio).

We'd then ensure that our students continue to practise Pythagoras' Theorem regularly, and wherever possible have the opportunity to use it in other topics that follow on the curriculum. Now that they 'know' Pythagoras' Theorem, they can (and should) use it all the time!

Overall we probably have somewhere between twelve and sixteen hours of highly engaging and worthwhile learning in our unit on Pythagoras' Theorem. Yet teachers are often spending less than four hours on this topic. Perhaps they think that their students can 'do Pythagoras' by the end of those four hours. But how can these students possibly have anything but a totally superficial level of knowledge when it has been taught so quickly? These students will have missed out on so many rich opportunities to develop as mathematicians.

What we need, in teaching Pythagoras' Theorem and indeed every other topic on the curriculum, is **more depth** and **less speed**.

21 Focus on the Nine Mathematical Basics

Julia Smith

Focus on the Nine Mathematical Basics, build strong mathematical foundations, develop mathematical fluency and dexterity and encourage maths practice, practice, practice – not until they get it right but until they cannot get it wrong!

If I could tell you only one thing, it would be that mathematical thinking depends upon fluency with the mathematical basics of addition, subtraction, multiplication, division, fractions, decimals, percentages, scale and ratio. This means that by focusing on the basics of maths you build a strong foundation. You wouldn't build a house on dodgy foundations so don't build a mathematician without those strong and firm foundations or 'cornerstones of maths' as Jemma Sherwood refers to in her Subject Knowledge Enhancement book.

William Emeny, in his connected maths curriculum posters, shows us the importance of the essential skills required to access as many topics on the GCSE curriculum as possible. Of the 164 topics in the GCSE curriculum there are 935 links where a link is the connection between two topics with one being the prior learning to be able to access it. When you visibly see the links back to the basics of adding and subtracting whole numbers, multiplying and dividing whole numbers it all makes complete sense. You really have never seen a GCSE maths curriculum quite like this one!

www.greatmathsteachingideas.com/2014/01/05/youve-never-seen-the-gcse-maths-curriculum-like-this-before/

There is a key phrase that arrived with the latest iteration of the GCSE maths curriculum from the DfE: 'any valid mathematical method will gain the marks'. This heralded the arrival of methods such as Vedic multiplication, the Egyptian method, Napier's Bones, stacked fractions and multifarious weird and wonderful yet fully valid mathematical methods. There is nothing new in many of them as they have been around for years and years in some case. But we don't think to put them into our teaching toolbox.

Most people tend to teach maths the way that they themselves were taught. Paraphrasing Stephen Chinn 'if a student cannot work it out one way then you have to find another way, or another way, or another until they can'. We need to build ourselves a mathematical toolbox of methods in order to help every single student.

John Hattie tells us that we are the only person paid to teach a student a particular skill. It's our job so if we if it doesn't work one way it's perhaps time to say. 'I don't think you learn it like that, have you seen this method?' From Paul Halmos we have 'the only way to learn mathematics is to do mathematics' but I'd add 'any which way that you can.'

Pam Harris, a Texan maths educator, has a great website called **www.mathisfigureoutable.com/**. She leads something called #mathstratchat weekly on Twitter where she posts up a calculation based on the maths basics and asks for contributions as to methods. The range of methods is always amazing, sometimes confusing, often ordinary but never dull! Well worth taking a look and joining in too.

Include **#MathStratChat** in your reply.

Which leads us to the Eight Effective Principles of Mathematics Teaching from Professor Malcolm Swan. His work has been seminal in the development of good maths teaching and producing great maths teachers. These three, of the eight, point me to the importance of getting the basics right but also to how we might do that.

- Emphasise methods rather than answers
- Use rich collaborative tasks
- Create connections between mathematical topics

Let us consider multiplication and times tables. Many students come to class lacking secure times tables knowledge. Many of us remember learning our times tables off by heart ... Monday morning with Mr Green and a times tables test...with a metronome ... and the board rubber whistling past your ear towards Paul Hammond at the back of the class who was simply miming nonsense like an out of tune Choir Boy that looked the part but hadn't got the skills. (Names have been changed to protect their dignity.)

I have a very sound mathematical foundation, being taught strictly and traditionally and yet once I went beyond 12×12, I reverted to the column method. I could always get the answer right as I had practised it until I couldn't get it wrong, not simply until I could get it right. However, knowing what I now know, I could be quicker – why wouldn't I want to be quicker! By allowing students to find the best way or the most efficient way, for them of calculating say 18 × 5 is something that they can work on together to come to a consensus about what works best for them.

There is also evidence from Pólya that suggests that problem solving is hampered if the action of solving the problem is distracted by calculating the basics; for example, the problem may require a calculation that involves 9 × 8 but if that doesn't come from fluency it holds up the problem and detracts from it, making the problem harder.

John Hattie reminds us that 'A method that suits the least able student will also suit the most able'. Nobody left behind. But as maths teachers we have to have our Mathematical Methods Toolbox that is over-spilling with golden nuggets that will tempt students to try and try again; magic keys that will unlock learning and lightbulbs that will ping and shine brightly once a student who couldn't do it before, now can. And then they can progress onto the higher mathematical demands. You cannot work with Standard Form unless you know how to work with multiplication.

Let's look at times tables again. 7 × 8 The answer is 56.
Some students learn this by recounting as a jaunty rhyme. (Think metronome here!)
'Seven eights are fifty six
Eight eights are sixty four'
Others look at the sequence 5678   56 = 7 × 8.

And we, as maths teachers, are never too old to learn! Ironically, I was 56 years old when I learned the following method for 7 × 8. Take a look at the method alongside, a method using number bonds to 10.

You may think that this is not the method for me but there's an important thing about our mathematical toolbox: IT IS NOT FOR US TO LIKE OR DISLIKE A METHOD. It might be just the method that suits the learner.

It's simply another way that will develop mathematical fluency. It's all a bit chicken and egg. In some cases, because a student can do something that they couldn't do easily before, they get curious. That's great. I can do it like that. How does that work?

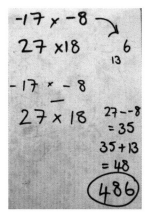

But the mad thing is that this method works for any multiplication! Try out 27 × 18.

A few more alternative methods for your toolbox:

Jo Morgan introduced me to the idea of stacked fractions in her most wonderful book *A Compendium of Mathematical Methods*. The process works on the basis of integer division.

4 ÷ 8 can be rewritten as 4/8, so 1/3 ÷ 3/7 can be rewritten as a stacked fraction.

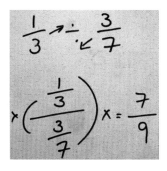

This is no more or no less a valid method as KFC or Keep Flip Change. There is no conceptual understanding with either but at least the student gets the answer right. Obviously, I would teach this skill much earlier as reciprocals but some students cannot get over the hump that is dividing fractions.

Ed Southall demonstrates how to teach using negative numbers by careful sequencing in his book *Yes, but why?* I can cite many occasions where I have spotted a neat trick or idea that helps build the basics. As a maths teacher you should spend time exploring a whole range of methods from some great educators, old and new. This will allow you to build that toolbox and keep adding to it as we explore further and discuss efficiencies with the basics.

And I shall leave you with the wisdom of Mickey Mouse...let's all get to the point where we don't need our fingers and toes in a maths lesson!

> *'Arithmetic is being able to count up to twenty without taking off your shoes.'*

22   *Make It Move*

Ben Sparks

"If a picture paints a thousand words…"

Try something for me. Open up a browser window and head to **geogebra.org** OR to **desmos.com**. Then click on 'START CALCULATOR' (or some equivalent – interfaces change all the time). Once you've got a blank looking graphing screen, type in $y = mx + c$ and hit enter.

Then find a tempting looking 'PLAY' ⏵ button near an "m" slider (which has hopefully appeared) and click it (Note 1).

I'd love to know how long you watch the result for. What questions occur to you? Does anything surprise you? (See Note 2)

Don't let me stop you here, if you want to go and play with those sliders then go right ahead, but we've established what I want to discuss here:

"If I could only tell you one thing… it would be to **make it move**"

In 2014 I wrote an article called 'Shifting the paradigm' for the Mathematical Association's *Mathematics In School* journal. In it I cast my mind back many years earlier to a fortuitous lesson during my PGCE training year in which I exploited *Geometer's Sketchpad* to make a diagram move. Writing the article helped me reflect on the power that moving diagrams had to provoke interest, motivate generalisation, and make an audience wonder what's going on. I've been consciously and unconsciously using this in my teaching ever since.

It's been 7 years since I wrote that article – the power of dynamic geometry and moving mathematical visualisation has never been more accessible to mathematics teachers and students alike than now. *Geogebra, Desmos & Autograph* are now all freely available at no cost to teachers or students, and can be used on phones, tablets, and computers anywhere we might wish.

I believe (as I did 7 years ago) that this constitutes as much of a revolution in mathematics (and its education) as the electronic calculator has produced in our subject since the 1970s.

A quick and accurate calculation is wonderful, useful, and - to anyone from more than a few generations ago - an almost miraculous thing. But we have been in a position now for many years where many people carry the ability to do these wondrous things around in their pocket, on a device, not even specially designed for that purpose (Note 3). Calculate the 12th root of 2 to 6dp (Note 4). Go! What did you reach for? Pen and paper?

Yes. Hand calculation skills and the ideas behind them remain important, but for speed, accuracy, and convenience absolutely no-one is arguing that we return to the days before this electronic assistance.

A quick and accurate picture of a function is similarly wonderful (it is, after all, the result of many quick and accurate calculations put together into a picture), and through the combination of web-access, smartphones, and freely accessible software we now are also in a position where anyone can access this power on a device they probably already own, or at a computer that can simply browse a website.

Yes. Sketching functions ourselves without assistance is useful (just like being able to perform a long division, or a manual square root), but for speed and accuracy I would always bet on a computer.

But I'm not just talking about the ability to graph things quickly and easily, as wonderful as that is. Specialist handheld graphing calculators followed a similar (if slower) path to numerical calculators, and have been widely available for many years. I would argue, however, that even now they remain the preserve of well-resourced school students, and many (most?) lie gathering dust in a drawer after school exams are done with. I'm sorry to say that mine has done exactly that. Why? I suggest it is because there are better, cheaper, more powerful tools available to mathematicians (whether inexperienced or experienced) and, what is more, these tools provide another dimension which I argue is crucial: **movement**. Before I annoy devotees of the fine graphical calculators that do now exist, I will clarify that I simply think that the function they perform has been superseded by software on more powerful devices. My case in point is that it *is possible* to make moving, dynamic, graphs on handheld graphical calculators, but it is slow, cumbersome and in my opinion, nullifies some of the benefits I discuss next.

I suggest that movement (in particular of a dynamic geometry/function diagram) in maths education is helpful for many reasons. Allow me to comment on three: *generalisation*, *attention*, and *interaction*.

First and foremost - mathematics at its heart is about *generalisation*. Algebra. Variables. Things that change (and things that don't). Making things move feels like a shortcut right to the heart of this matter.

When we move from specialising to generalising we often do it through exposure to repeated examples. Consider a set of examples of straight line graphs with their equations $y = 3x + 1$, $y = -2x + 2$, $y = \frac{1}{3}x + 2$. The classic mathematical prompt of "What's the same, and what is different?" is a natural way in.

Now consider the dynamic graph I asked you to build at the start of this piece. The prompt may morph slightly to "What's staying the same, and what is changing?" but it feels an even more natural question. Indeed it feels like a formal phrasing of the almost involuntary (if less articulate) cry of "Sir, what's it doing?" The utterance of which, in my own classroom experience, from some student, is only a matter of time.

Repeated specific examples can direct your attention to a general conclusion. An animation is essentially a sequence of frames of specific examples - and general conclusions jump out. But it seems to me that an animation like this becomes more than the sum of its parts. In our example the animation of the graph as m changes might immediately communicate an idea that the coefficient of x controls the slope or gradient (this was my intention in showing a class). But an animation like this can also make you notice more, and fit more information into a fledgling generalisation. In the case in point there are several examples of this - perhaps a sense that a 'zero' gradient (a horizontal line) is not just a special case, but part of the continuum of possible gradients, perhaps a sense that a vertical gradient is not possible with this form of equation (you can 'feel' a limit behaviour if you allow the gradient to change smoothly to very high values, since the visual change gets obviously slower).

These observations often arise unplanned, from observers, in a way that repeated construction of examples seems to not reveal as easily.

In short, a moving picture (especially where the particular movement has been carefully and deliberately chosen) can provoke generalisation – and further questioning and interest – among an audience or classroom, in a way which I find both gratifying and useful as a teacher. After all, to paraphrase a much used quote of John Mason's, "A lesson without the opportunity to generalise is not a mathematics lesson".

Secondly I mentioned **attention**. To me this feels like an issue for educators (or entertainers) more than mathematicians. Gaining, holding, and directing an observer's attention. These are crucial parts of a presentation. I hasten to add that a teacher's role goes far beyond presentation, but it is an important tool in our work. The ability to easily show a pertinent (possibly even 'bespoke') moving image is a powerful way to capture and hold a group's attention. Movement does something to our attention. Notice a toddler's interest in a moving picture on a TV screen compared to a single static picture. Notice how distracting a moving pop-up advert on a website is, compared to a static advert. Think of most TV documentaries, which often include a shot of a static image. You will often see a pan and zoom effect, guiding your eye towards a focal point, or breathing life into the static photograph (this has become known as the Ken Burns effect after the American filmmaker). However cliché the effect becomes, it works. Something moving makes you look, and keep looking. Dynamic geometry/graphing is a powerful way for mathematics educators to make use of this. The example of our moving gradient is simple, but I would be prepared to stake a decent amount of money that the attention of students tends to stay longer on the moving diagram than even a series of static ones. Once the attention stays, the questions (and hopefully generalisations) seem to come more naturally.

Movement does something to our *attention*, and therefore whoever is in control of the movement arguably has some control over our attention.

This brings me to my third point – **interaction**. I suggested that whoever is controlling the movement has some power over the attention, but attention and focus seems to spike if the control of the movement is actually handed over to the observer. The increase in attention from a static picture to a moving picture is quite a jump, but another jump happens when interaction between the observer and the moving picture is enabled. An obvious trio of examples might be a photograph, a film, and a computer game. The dynamic geometry packages I mentioned earlier do not simply just enable mathematical pictures to move, they enable live interactions and experiments. This can be powerful when used to create animations, even more powerful when a presenter interacts with a picture 'live', and still more powerful when an audience is given control.

In a classroom context this could occur if control of the mouse pointer is temporarily given to a student (as part of a whole class discussion) - for example: a teacher using our gradient example displaying $y = x + 2$ hands a wireless mouse to a student and asks them to "try to find a gradient that is negative, but not as steep as this one" by dragging the 'm' slider.

Alternatively the classroom context might involve each student accessing the interactive graph on their own device, or school computer, possibly even building the file themselves. Here we come back to the argument for getting this tech into the hands of the students themselves. Handheld graphical calculators can do this, at some expense. However, when there exists software which is more accessible, more powerful, and more useful outside of an exam situation, I think we have to question whether expensive dedicated devices are the best thing to invest time and money in.

The point is that the power to work in this way is now more available than ever. Both by interacting with pre-made examples and creating their own examples, learners can access the startling and attention-grabbing power of mathematical movement themselves. Learners' interaction with, and ownership of, the examples can be captivating.

I do not claim this is an exhaustive list of benefits of mathematical movement, but if seeing generalisation in moving images, helping to gain and hold attention, and allowing playful interaction were the only benefits, they would be still enough to keep me evangelical about these tools!

I have focussed mostly on the benefits to the learner. I could say more (even if only anecdotally) about the benefits to the educators (also learners!) themselves. But if I could tell *myself* one thing about my mathematical understanding when I was starting out as a teacher it might be something along the lines of a phrase that they found Richard Feynman had left written on his own blackboard after he died. He said "What I cannot create, I do not understand". I have found Dynamic Geometry packages to be remarkable tools to help me 'create' bits of mathematics, tinkering with them until I feel like I understand. Things that move and help me generalise, things that move and help me demonstrate, things that move and simply delight me. For me it has become another tool, alongside the time-honoured pen and paper and the more recently obvious calculator tools to 'get my hands dirty' with mathematics, and in doing so grapple with my understanding, and the understanding of others. I'm glad that I get to do and teach mathematics in a time when these tools are available.

They say a picture paints a thousand words. How much more can a moving picture do?

Notes

(1) Here's one I made earlier, in case you need a shortcut, but I recommend making it yourself: **www.geogebra.org/m/sfpz24jk**

(2) For example, at this point in a lesson a year 9 student immediately asked me why the animation of the slope changed more quickly 'when it was flatter' than 'when it was steeper'. The ensuing discussion among the class lasted considerably longer than I expected. I'll leave you to ponder how you might have handled this yourself...

(3) I am talking about smartphones, but kudos to those of you still carrying handheld calculators around with you.

(4) Respect, where it's due, to the creators of the equal temperament musical scale.

23   *Be Kind, Be Bothered, Care*

Kathryn Greenhalgh

This is about an ethos for teaching mathematics and how keeping this a priority in your approach will mean you will always succeed in the end.

I have interviewed a huge number of mathematics teachers over the last 16 years: for unpromoted posts, seconds in department, heads of department, lead teachers and Directors of mathematics. The one thing that will get you the job, over everything else, over great subject knowledge, over a really engaging activity, over a beautifully-designed set of questions that reveal misconceptions, over a well-thought-through constructed sequence of small steps that enables students to have that 'light-bulb' moment and over many other fabulous things that I love to see at an interview, is if you make me cry.

That may sound sinister, and is quite the opposite – and I don't mean full on bawl (although that did happen quite recently, to the point where we had to stop, to get tissues, for me and the other two interviewers and yes, he did get the job!) – I mean make me well up and my heart feel warm.

> You will make me cry if I see you approach the quietest child in the room who looks nervous and disengaged and you somehow make them smile, feel comfortable and feel able to access the work.

> You will make me cry if you talk to the students with gentle kindness and respect that gives them the feeling that you care.

> You will make me cry if you are scanning the room whilst delivering the concept to look for the blank faces that say 'I don't understand' while pretending that they do, and you handle those students in a way that no other students would know they didn't get it, without drawing attention to them.

> You will make me cry if you recount the time you knew your lessons weren't working for a particular class of students, so you sat at home every night for a week designing lessons, and trying them out until you found a formula that worked for them – and when you did, you watched them learning and you felt amazing.

You will make me cry if you talk with passion about how a mathematics qualification can transform a student's life.
You will make me cry if, when telling me about a specific time where you really helped a student grasp a concept, because you had gone away and really tried to work out why they didn't understand and looked for a more accessible way in for them, and while telling me you find yourself welling up. Because you cared. Because you are kind.

If you look at the Job Specification for any mathematics teacher position, I challenge you to find 'are kind' in the essential criteria, and yet it is *the* most essential quality to have for the job. If you are kind you will always be thoughtful about how you approach your lessons and be keen to continually improve them. If you are bothered, you will always find a way. In the role of a teacher, being kind is inextricably linked to really caring that the students learn.

Really caring means that you will go that extra mile to make sure that they grasp a concept.

Really caring means passionately wanting those students to experience the same joy of maths that you do.

Really caring means that you know what currency a mathematics qualification will be for them when they leave school and strive to ensure they achieve it.

Really caring is knowing how much understanding mathematics can change a child's life, give them confidence and help them pave a pathway to a better life, so everything you do, every lesson you plan, every interaction you have is about opening that door to understanding mathematics.

Teaching is not an easy option as a job; being a maths teacher, potentially even less so. Some teachers can make it look ridiculously easy and there really are 'natural born teachers'. But when you actually talk to these teachers, the reason why they make it look so easy is because they've worked so hard to get it right. They have thought really hard about their planning, because they are really, genuinely bothered that the students understand. They think hard about 'Why do they not understand? I need to find out why, work out why'. They care.

They love to give their students the 'gift' of understanding mathematics. They are kind.

It is a proper vocation. The rewards are great. But on the dark days in November, when the marking is piling up, the students are restless and wound up by anything because it happens to be a bit windy outside; when you can't get through a lesson that you spent ages planning because there's a spider in the corner or something happened at break and all the students want to do is argue about it; when a student swears at you out of frustration, but really it's not at you, it's at the world because he's having to deal with something far more important to him at the moment, it is hard to be generous, magnanimous, kind. But if you are, and if you keep that at the forefront of everything that you do, you will be rewarded.

During my dad's father-of-the-bride speech, he talked about how he had met one of the pupils I used to teach over 20 years ago. They'd got talking, unusual surname, 'I used to have a maths teacher called that' etc., etc. My dad went on to say how this man could clearly remember me as a really young teacher. At this point I started cringing, wondering what NQT disaster story was going to come out to give everyone a good laugh. But what he actually said was how this young man had told him 'She was one of the good ones, she was. She really cared.' I did well up a bit, I won't lie.

Be kind, be bothered, care.

Contributors

Ed Southall @edsouthall (Editor)

Ed is the maths lead for Oak National Academy and the University of Huddersfield PGCE programme. He is the author of *Yes, But Why? Teaching for Understanding in Mathematics, Geometry Snacks* and *Geometry Juniors.*

Catriona Agg @cshearer41

Catriona is a secondary maths teacher and Post-16 Lead for Venn Essex Maths Hub. She spends far too much of her free time creating and colouring in geometry puzzles.

Sam Blatherwick @blatherwick_sam

Sam is Head of Maths at Ashby School in North West Leicestershire.

Stephen Cavadino @srcav

Stephen is a deputy faculty director at an 11-18 secondary school in West Yorkshire.

Kyle Evans @KyleDEvans

Kyle Evans is an award-winning maths presenter, teacher, and author of *Maths Tricks to Blow Your Mind.*

Nate Evans @TheMrEMachine

Nate Evans is a Teacher of Mathematics and Head of Year at a secondary school in Bradford.

Colin Foster @colinfoster77

Colin is a reader in mathematics education at the Mathematics Education Centre at Loughborough University. He is the editor-in-chief of the *International Journal of Mathematical Education in Science and Technology* and the 2022-23 President of The Mathematical Association.

Tom Francome @TFrancome

Tom is senior fellow at the Centre for Mathematical Cognition in the Mathematics Education Centre at Loughborough University.

Sudeep Gokarakonda @boss_maths

Sudeep started teaching in 2008 and has worked in roles up to Head of Maths in London secondary schools. He creates and shares mathematical applets and other resources online, and enjoys writing mysteries in his spare time.

Kathryn Greenhalgh @kag6maths

Kathryn is the senior director of mathematics at Outwood Grange Academies Trust, and the Yorkshire and the Humber Maths Hub lead.

Daniel Griller @puzzlecritic

Daniel Griller is a teacher and author. His inventions have appeared in the British Maths Olympiad, *The Guardian*, on Radio 4, and in the publications *Elastic Numbers* and *Problem Solving in GCSE Mathematics*.

Jonathan Hall @studymaths

Jonathan is the creator of MathsBot, CPD Lead for Complete Mathematics and Lead Practitioner at Leeds City Academy.

Peter Mattock @MrMattock

Peter Mattock is an Assistant Headteacher, Secondary Teaching for Mastery Lead and author of *Visible Maths: Using Representations and Structure to Enhance Mathematics Teaching in Schools*.

Jo Morgan @mathsjem

Jo is a maths teacher and Assistant Principal at Harris Academy Sutton. She writes the website **resourceaholic.com** where she shares teaching ideas and resources for secondary mathematics. Jo is the author of the book *A Compendium of Mathematical Methods*. She is a regular guest on Mr Barton's podcast and an enthusiastic collector of old maths textbooks.

Martin Noon @letsgetmathing

Martin Noon is a freelance content writer for mathematics education and teaches part-time. He has written textbook and online content for companies such as Pearson, OUP, York Press Ltd, Mathigon and Third Space Learning.

Paul Rowlandson @Mr_Rowlandson

Paul Rowlandson is a secondary school maths teacher, middle leader and author of blog site ponderingplanning.wordpress.com

Jemma Sherwood @jemmaths

Jemma is the Senior Lead Practitioner for Mathematics at the Ormiston Academies Trust. She is the author of *How to Enhance Your Mathematics Subject Knowledge* and student workbooks.

Jo Sibley @JusSumChick

Jo has taught maths for more than 25 years and is a Maths Education Support Specialist at MEI, designing, developing and managing online training programmes for the AMSP.

Chris Smith @aap03102

Chris is a former Scottish Teacher of the Year who writes a weekly Maths newsletter for over 4000 subscribers (become one by emailing aap03012@gmail.com). You might also have spotted him on TV when Team Smith won the 2019 BBC show *Family Brain Games* hosted by Dara Ó Briain.

Julia Smith @tessmaths

Julia is a maths teacher trainer and author with a host of organisations including BBC *Bitesize*, AQA, Edexcel, Cambridge University Press, Collins and the ETF.

Ben Sparks @SparksMaths

Ben is a mathematician, musician, teacher, and public speaker. He gives maths talks and workshops around the world, to students, teachers, and the general public, and is also a regular contributor to the *Numberphile* YouTube channel.

Eddie Woo @misterwootube

Eddie Woo is an Australian maths teacher, author, tv presenter and YouTube star with over one million subscribers to his maths videos at **www.youtube.com/c/misterwootube/**